# Contents

C000046358

The Photocopy Masters are of three levels of difficulty,
- ● basic work
- ●● for all children
- ●●● enrichment and extension

Name _____

6-digit numbers

Write the value of the digit 8 in each number.

I. 476 823 $\longrightarrow$

2. 708 436 $\longrightarrow$

3. 352 178 $\longrightarrow$

4. 76 584 $\longrightarrow$

5. 83 472 $\longrightarrow$

6. 805 613 $\longrightarrow$

Write the value of the digit 3 in each number.

7. 231 407 $\longrightarrow$

8. 503 620 $\longrightarrow$

9. 129 430 $\longrightarrow$

10. 78 320 $\longrightarrow$

II. 326 040 $\longrightarrow$

12. 400 235 $\longrightarrow$

I

6-digit numbers

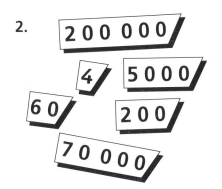

Add these.

1.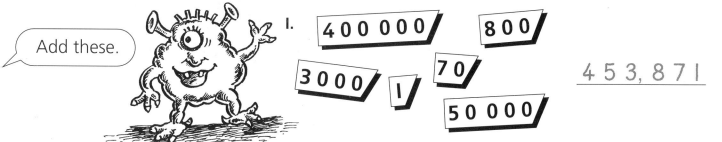

   4 0 0 0 0 0   8 0 0

   3 0 0 0   1   7 0
                      5 0 0 0 0

   _4 5 3, 8 7 1_

2. 2 0 0 0 0 0
   4   5 0 0 0
   6 0   2 0 0
   7 0 0 0 0

   _____

3. 7 0   9
   3 0 0
            6 0 0 0
   8 0 0 0 0
       3 0 0 0 0 0

   _____

4.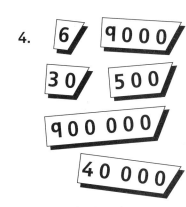

   6   9 0 0 0
   3 0   5 0 0
   9 0 0 0 0 0
       4 0 0 0 0

   _____

5. 9 0 0 0   2 0
   8 0 0   4 0 0 0 0
   1 0 0 0 0 0

   _____

6. 2 0   7 0 0 0
   4 0 0 0 0 0   3
   5 0 0 0 0

   _____

7. 5 0 0 0 0
            9 0
   3 0 0   1
   6 0 0 0 0 0

   _____

8. 2 0 0 0
   1 0 0   6
   8 0 0 0 0 0
       5 0 0 0 0

   _____

9. 3 0 0
            4 0
   2 0 0 0
            1 0 0 0 0 0
   1 0 0 0 0

   _____

10. 3 0 0 0
    1   7 0
    5 0 0 0 0 0

    _____

5-digit numbers

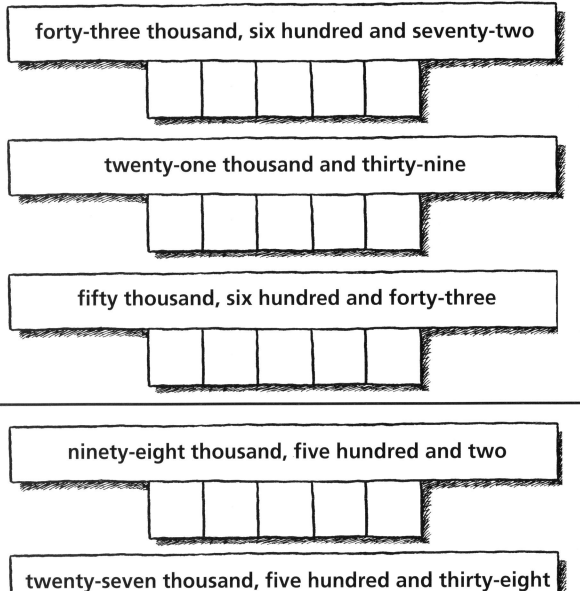

forty-three thousand, six hundred and seventy-two

twenty-one thousand and thirty-nine

fifty thousand, six hundred and forty-three

ninety-eight thousand, five hundred and two

twenty-seven thousand, five hundred and thirty-eight

sixty-four thousand, two hundred and seventy-one

Teacher's instructions
A game for two players, one using the top three numbers, the other using the bottom three. Shuffle the number cards and place them face down in a pile. Take turns to reveal a card. If possible, write the number in one of your boxes. If this is not possible, then you must try to write it in one of your opponent's boxes. Replace the card at random in the pile. The winner is the first to have all three numbers completed.

3

Materials
2 sets of number cards (0 to 9)

Name _____

Nearest thousand

Make a 4-digit number using each digit at the top of the three columns.

Nearest thousand	④ ⑨ ⑦ ①	② ⑤ ③ ⑧	⑥ ③ ① ⑨	Use your own 4 digits
1000				
2000				
3000				
4000				
5000				
6000				
7000				
8000				
9000				
10 000				

Name _____

Nearest hundred

Use one of each of these number cards to make 4-digit numbers which have these numbers as their nearest hundreds.

1. ⬚⬚⬚⬚ ⟶ 2700

2. ⬚⬚⬚⬚ ⟶ 4700

3. ⬚⬚⬚⬚ ⟶ 7200

4. ⬚⬚⬚⬚ ⟶ 8300

5. ⬚⬚⬚⬚ ⟶ 8700

6. ⬚⬚⬚⬚ ⟶ 2800

7. ⬚⬚⬚⬚ ⟶ 8200

8. ⬚⬚⬚⬚ ⟶ 4800

9. ⬚⬚⬚⬚ ⟶ 7800

10. ⬚⬚⬚⬚ ⟶ 7300

11. ⬚⬚⬚⬚ ⟶ 2900

12. ⬚⬚⬚⬚ ⟶ 8400

13. ⬚⬚⬚⬚ ⟶ 4300

14. ⬚⬚⬚⬚ ⟶ 2500

15. ⬚⬚⬚⬚ ⟶ 7500

16. ⬚⬚⬚⬚ ⟶ 4900

Name _____

Nearest million

Use number cards to make 7- and 8-digit numbers.
Round them to the nearest million, nearest hundred
thousand and nearest ten thousand.

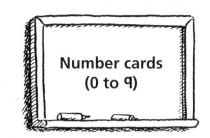

**Number cards
(0 to 9)**

Number	Nearest million	Nearest hundred thousand	Nearest ten thousand
1 573 264	2 000 000	1 600 000	1 570 000

Name _____

Dividing

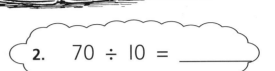

Complete these.

1. 21 ÷ 7 = _____

2. 70 ÷ 10 = _____

3. 21 ÷ 3 = _____

4. 18 ÷ 2 = _____

5. 24 ÷ 4 = _____

6. 42 ÷ 6 = _____

7. 18 ÷ 6 = _____

8. 35 ÷ 5 = _____

9. 28 ÷ 4 = _____

10. 16 ÷ 8 = _____

11. 40 ÷ 8 = _____

12. 27 ÷ 9 = _____

13. 45 ÷ 5 = _____

14. 35 ÷ 7 = _____

15. 49 ÷ 7 = _____

16. 30 ÷ 3 = _____

17. 40 ÷ 4 = _____

18. 63 ÷ 9 = _____

19. 16 ÷ 2 = _____

20. 36 ÷ 6 = _____

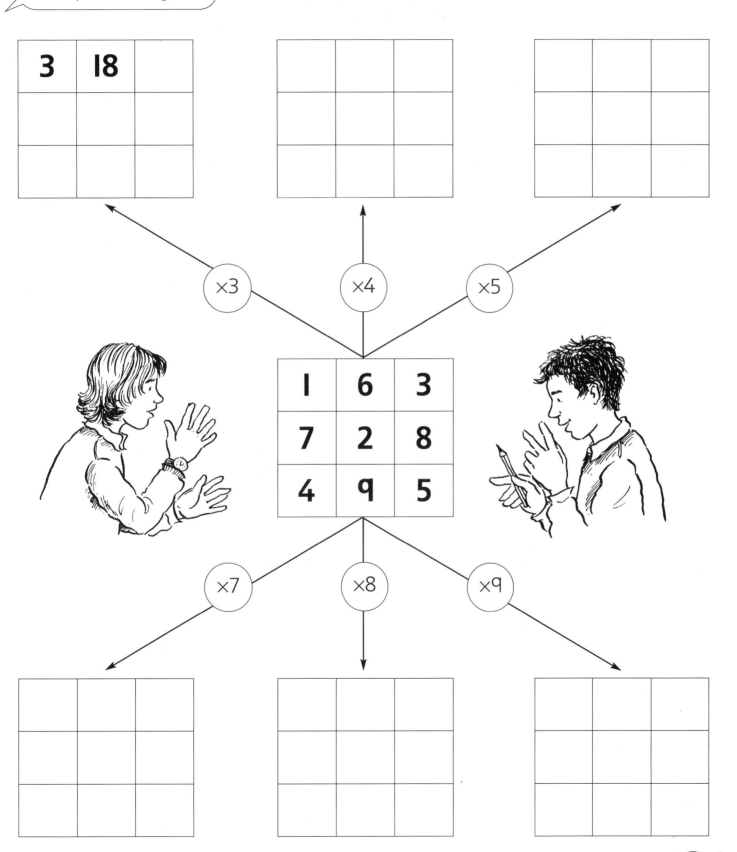

Name _____

Multiplication practice

Complete each grid.

3	18	

×3   ×4   ×5

1	6	3
7	2	8
4	9	5

×7   ×8   ×9

8

Name _____

Problem page

I. There are 45 players in the basketball club. How many 5-a-side teams can be made?

2. Seats for the school play are arranged in rows of 8. There are 9 rows altogether. How many people can be seated?

3. Tennis balls are packed in tubes of 6. If Andre buys 8 tubes, how many tennis balls will he have? Each tube costs £3. What is the cost of each ball? How much change will Andre get from £30?

4. The school holidays last for six weeks. How many days off school do the children have, including weekends?

5. Amanda sleeps for 8 hours every day. How many hours does she sleep in a week? Michael sleeps for 7 hours a day on weekdays and 9 hours a day at weekends. How many hours does he sleep in a week?

6. Sol has 54p to spend. How many 6p stickers can he buy? How much more money would he need to buy 8 stickers costing 9p each?

7. Kazuo bought 6 packs of 7 postcards to send to his friends. His sister bought 8 packs of 5 postcards. Who bought the most cards? How many more?

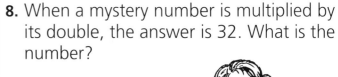

8. When a mystery number is multiplied by its double, the answer is 32. What is the number?

Name _____

Remainders

Teacher's instructions
A game for two players.
Take turns to choose a number on the board. Throw the dice, then divide the
number on the board by the number on the dice. Collect cubes to match the
remainder. Check each other's divisions, then cover your chosen number with a
counter. If you throw a '1', then throw again. When all the numbers have been
covered, see who has collected the most cubes.

Materials
A dice
Counters
Cubes

10

Name _____

Dividing

Divide 23 by each of the numbers 2 to 10, writing the remainder as a fraction each time.

1. $23 \div 2 = \underline{11\frac{1}{2}}$

2. $23 \div 3 = $ _____

3. $23 \div 4 = $ _____

4. $23 \div 5 = $ _____

5. $23 \div 6 = $ _____

6. $23 \div 7 = $ _____

7. $23 \div 8 = $ _____

8. $23 \div 9 = $ _____

9. $23 \div 10 = $ _____

Choose your own number to divide.

10. _____ $\div 2 = $ _____

11. _____ $\div 3 = $ _____

12. _____ $\div 4 = $ _____

13. _____ $\div 5 = $ _____

14. _____ $\div 6 = $ _____

15. _____ $\div 7 = $ _____

16. _____ $\div 8 = $ _____

17. _____ $\div 9 = $ _____

18. _____ $\div 10 = $ _____

Name _____

Dividing by 10

Complete each division. Write the answer as a decimal.

1. $70 \div 10 = \underline{\ 7 \cdot 0\ }$

2. $140 \div 10 = \underline{\hspace{2cm}}$

3. $53 \div 10 = \underline{\hspace{2cm}}$

4. $46 \div 10 = \underline{\hspace{2cm}}$

5. $\dfrac{48}{10} = \underline{\hspace{2cm}}$

6. $\dfrac{79}{10} = \underline{\hspace{2cm}}$

7. $580 \div 10 = \underline{\hspace{2cm}}$

8. $800 \div 10 = \underline{\hspace{2cm}}$

9. $476 \div 10 = \underline{\hspace{2cm}}$

10. $8 \div 10 = \underline{\hspace{2cm}}$

Write the missing numbers.

11. $57 \div 10 =$

12. $\div 10 = 9 \cdot 1$

13. $\div 10 = 54 \cdot 0$

14. $\div 10 = 78 \cdot 0$

15. $\div 10 = 63 \cdot 9$

16. $\div 10 = 12 \cdot 5$

17. $\dfrac{}{10} = 7 \cdot 8$

18. $\dfrac{}{10} = 57 \cdot 6$

19. $\div 10 = 0 \cdot 4$

20. $\div 10 = 0 \cdot 9$

Name _____

Halving

Complete the grids.

162	96	84
122	176	154
58	184	112

460	1420	540
1720	980	1640
1880	720	1040

700	2600	4800
4600	5800	1400
3000	3600	7800

Name _____

Two doubles

Choose two numbers from the grid.

Double them, then add them together.

Which two numbers, when doubled, add together to make these scores?

127	276	198
178	146	97
312	256	235

    double   double

1. [146] add [127] ⟶ Score 546

2. [   ] add [   ] ⟶ Score 878

3. [   ] add [   ] ⟶ Score 806

4. [   ] add [   ] ⟶ Score 980

5. [   ] add [   ] ⟶ Score 826

6. [   ] add [   ] ⟶ Score 762

7. [   ] add [   ] ⟶ Score 550

8. [   ] add [   ] ⟶ Score 1136

14

Name _____

Calculations

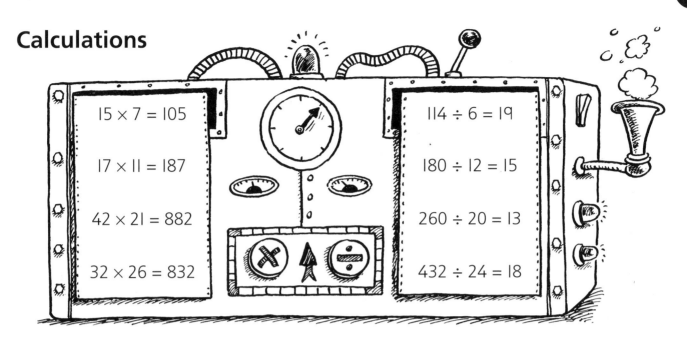

$15 \times 7 = 105$

$17 \times 11 = 187$

$42 \times 21 = 882$

$32 \times 26 = 832$

$114 \div 6 = 19$

$180 \div 12 = 15$

$260 \div 20 = 13$

$432 \div 24 = 18$

Use the eight calculations above to help you write a calculation for these answers.

1. $15 = \underline{105 \div 7}$

2. $11 = \underline{\hspace{2cm}}$

3. $432 = \underline{\hspace{2cm}}$

4. $12 = \underline{\hspace{2cm}}$

5. $21 = \underline{\hspace{2cm}}$

6. $20 = \underline{\hspace{2cm}}$

7. $180 = \underline{\hspace{2cm}}$

8. $32 = \underline{\hspace{2cm}}$

9. $114 = \underline{\hspace{2cm}}$

10. $7 = \underline{\hspace{2cm}}$

11. $24 = \underline{\hspace{2cm}}$

12. $6 = \underline{\hspace{2cm}}$

13. $42 = \underline{\hspace{2cm}}$

14. $260 = \underline{\hspace{2cm}}$

15. $26 = \underline{\hspace{2cm}}$

16. $17 = \underline{\hspace{2cm}}$

Name _____

Mixed numbers

Shade the fractions shown.

1.
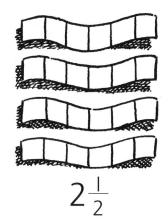

$2\frac{1}{2}$

2.
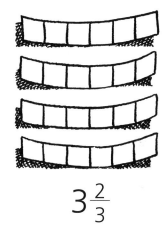

$3\frac{2}{3}$

3.
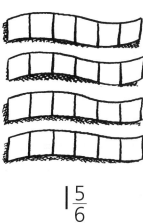

$1\frac{5}{6}$

4.
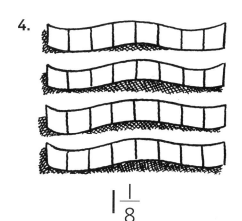

$1\frac{1}{8}$

5.
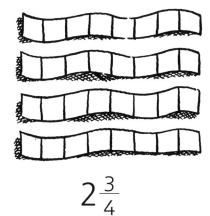

$2\frac{3}{4}$

6.
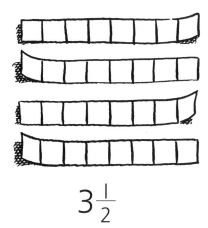

$3\frac{1}{2}$

7.
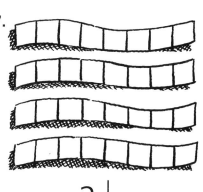

$2\frac{1}{4}$

8.
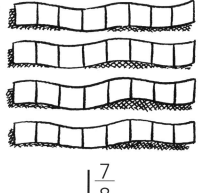

$1\frac{7}{8}$

9.
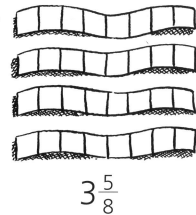

$3\frac{5}{8}$

Name _____

Fractions

Change each mixed number to a fraction.

1. $3\frac{4}{5} = \dfrac{}{5}$

2. $1\frac{2}{3} = \dfrac{}{3}$

3. $4\frac{5}{8} = \dfrac{}{8}$

4. $3\frac{1}{2} = \dfrac{}{2}$

5. $5\frac{3}{4} = \dfrac{}{4}$

6. $2\frac{2}{7} = \dfrac{}{7}$

7. $6\frac{1}{3} = \dfrac{}{3}$

8. $9\frac{5}{6} = \dfrac{}{6}$

9. $7\frac{4}{5} = \dfrac{}{}$

10. $11\frac{1}{2} = \dfrac{}{}$

11. $4\frac{3}{10} = \dfrac{}{}$

12. $10\frac{2}{3} = \dfrac{}{}$

13. $3\frac{3}{4} = \dfrac{}{}$

14. $8\frac{7}{10} = \dfrac{}{}$

15. $4\frac{2}{5} = \dfrac{}{}$

16. $19\frac{1}{4} = \dfrac{}{}$

Name _____

Equivalent fractions

Complete the equivalent fractions.

1.

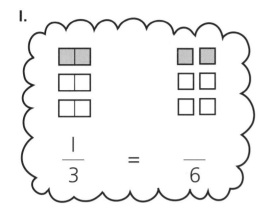

$$\frac{1}{3} = \frac{\quad}{6}$$

2.

$$\underline{\quad} = \underline{\quad}$$

3.

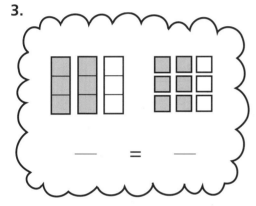

$$\underline{\quad} = \underline{\quad}$$

4.

$$\underline{\quad} = \underline{\quad}$$

5.

$$\underline{\quad} = \underline{\quad}$$

6.

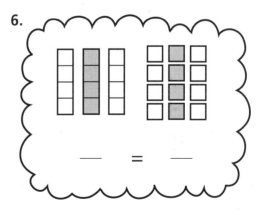

$$\underline{\quad} = \underline{\quad}$$

7.

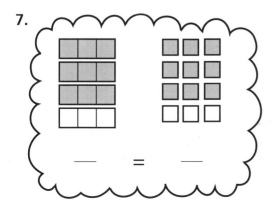

$$\underline{\quad} = \underline{\quad}$$

8.

$$\underline{\quad} = \underline{\quad}$$

Name _____

Equivalent fractions

Complete the pairs of equivalent fractions.

1. $\dfrac{1}{2} = \dfrac{\bigcirc}{4}$

2. $\dfrac{1}{3} = \dfrac{\bigcirc}{6}$

3. $\dfrac{\bigcirc}{9} = \dfrac{1}{3}$

4. $\dfrac{\bigcirc}{8} = \dfrac{3}{4}$

5. $\dfrac{4}{8} = \dfrac{\bigcirc}{2}$

6. $\dfrac{1}{5} = \dfrac{\bigcirc}{15}$

7. $\dfrac{\bigcirc}{3} = \dfrac{4}{6}$

8. $\dfrac{3}{5} = \dfrac{\bigcirc}{10}$

9. $\dfrac{5}{6} = \dfrac{\bigcirc}{12}$

10. $\dfrac{\bigcirc}{12} = \dfrac{3}{4}$

11. $\dfrac{\bigcirc}{7} = \dfrac{2}{14}$

12. $\dfrac{3}{8} = \dfrac{\bigcirc}{16}$

13. $\dfrac{2}{10} = \dfrac{\bigcirc}{5}$

14. $\dfrac{\bigcirc}{5} = \dfrac{16}{20}$

15. $\dfrac{1}{2} = \dfrac{\bigcirc}{24}$

16. $\dfrac{2}{3} = \dfrac{\bigcirc}{9}$

Problem page

1. When a mystery number is doubled, then doubled again, the answer is 144. What is the number?

2. 53 chocolates are to be shared equally between 8 children. How many chocolates will each child get? How many will be left over?

3. When a mystery number is multiplied by itself, the answer is 24 less than 60. What is the number?

4. Craig has a bag of 43 marbles to share equally between himself and 3 other friends. How many marbles do they each get? How many marbles are left over?

5. What number can be divided exactly by 7 and by 8, and is different from 40 by 16?

6. Colin the chef bakes some cakes for a party. He bakes 5 trays each holding 8 cakes, and 7 trays each holding 9 cakes. How many cakes does he bake altogether? How many are left over if 20 children at the party eat 5 each?

7. A 2-digit number can be divided exactly by 8. Both of its digits are even and they have a difference of 4. What is the number?

8. A mystery number leaves a remainder of 2 when divided by 7. The number is between 50 and 55. What is the number?

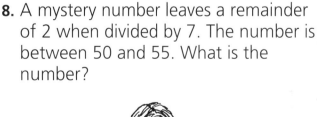

Name _____

Halves and quarters

Complete each sentence.

1.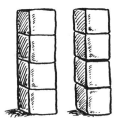

$\dfrac{1}{2}$ of ____ = ____

2.

$\dfrac{1}{4}$ of ____ = ____

3.

$\dfrac{1}{4}$ of ____ = ____

4.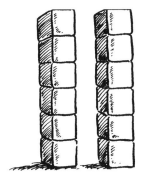

$\dfrac{1}{2}$ of ____ = ____

5.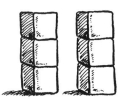

$\dfrac{1}{2}$ of ____ = ____

6.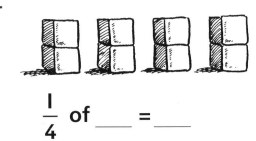

$\dfrac{1}{4}$ of ____ = ____

7.

$\dfrac{1}{4}$ of ____ = ____

8.

$\dfrac{1}{2}$ of ____ = ____

Name _____

Fractions of amounts

Complete these.

1. $\frac{1}{2}$ of 16 = ☐

2. $\frac{1}{4}$ of 20 = ☐

3. $\frac{1}{3}$ of 15 = ☐

4. $\frac{3}{4}$ of 24 = ☐

5. $\frac{2}{3}$ of 9 = ☐

6. $\frac{1}{5}$ of 10 = ☐

7. $\frac{2}{7}$ of 14 = ☐

8. $\frac{3}{8}$ of 24 = ☐

9. $\frac{2}{5}$ of 15 = ☐

10. $\frac{3}{10}$ of 20 = ☐

11. $\frac{1}{8}$ of 8 = ☐

12. $\frac{3}{7}$ of 21 = ☐

13. $\frac{4}{10}$ of 30 = ☐

14. $\frac{3}{5}$ of 20 = ☐

15. $\frac{7}{10}$ of 50 = ☐

16. $\frac{5}{8}$ of 8 = ☐

17. $\frac{4}{5}$ of 25 = ☐

18. $\frac{5}{6}$ of 12 = ☐

19. $\frac{4}{7}$ of 28 = ☐

20. $\frac{7}{8}$ of 16 = ☐

Name _____

Adding to the next 10 and 100

Use number cards 7, 3 and 6. | Write all the different 2-digit numbers you can make. | What must be added to make the next 10?

1.  next 10 _____

2. next 10 _____

3. next 10 _____

4. next 10 _____

5. next 10 _____

6. next 10 _____

Use number cards 7, 5 and 8. | Write all the different 3-digit numbers you can make. | What must be added to make the next 10 and 100?

7.
next 10 _____
next 100 _____

8.
next 10 _____
next 100 _____

9.
next 10 _____
next 100 _____

10.
next 10 _____
next 100 _____

11.
next 10 _____
next 100 _____

12.
next 10 _____
next 100 _____

23

Name _____

Adding to I00

The numbers in each pair total I00. Write the missing numbers.

1.

2.

3.

4.

5.

6.

7.

8.

9.

10.

11.

12.

13.

14.

15.

16.

17.

18.

19.

20.

21.

22.

23.

24.

Name _____

The next thousand

Write the missing number.

1. ( ) + 1000 = 4000   2. ( ) + 500 = 6000

3. ( ) + 700 = 7000   4. ( ) + 600 = 1000

5. ( ) + 800 = 2000   6. ( ) + 900 = 3000

7. ( ) + 450 = 2000   8. ( ) + 750 = 8000

9. ( ) + 250 = 1000   10. ( ) + 550 = 4000

11. ( ) + 650 = 6000   12. ( ) + 750 = 3000

13. ( ) + 250 = 5000   14. ( ) + 950 = 8000

15. ( ) + 550 = 7000   16. ( ) + 50 = 5000

17. ( ) + 150 = 9000   18. ( ) + 350 = 10 000

19. ( ) + 850 = 9000   20. ( ) + 150 = 4000

Name _____

Adding

Write the total of each row and column.

80	70	20
60	50	40
10	30	90

60	90	20
50	40	90
90	30	10

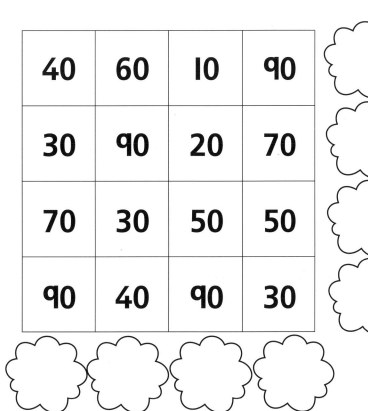

40	60	10	90
30	90	20	70
70	30	50	50
90	40	90	30

26

Name _____

Totals

Write the total of each set.

I.   19   20
   32

total _____

2.   35   37
   33

total _____

3.   31   29
   42   15

total _____

4.   24   32   46
   19

total _____

5.   26   34   28
   19

total _____

6.   14   28   15
   22

total _____

7.   16   26   43
   15

total _____

8.   33   45   67
   25   18

total _____

9.   19   28   53
   27   42

total _____

10.   37   63
   25   19

total _____

II.   47   72   53
   28   56

total _____

12.   64   20   19
   72   36

total _____

Name _____

Adding 4-digit numbers

Estimate the total, then add.

I.
```
    2  7  I  6
 +  4  2  3  0
 _____
```

2.
```
    3  5  8  5
 +  5  6  5  7
 _____
```

3.
```
    2  4  4  I
 +  4  8  9  3
 _____
```

4.
```
    6  3  3  6
 +  2  9  7  6
 _____
```

5.
```
    4  2  2  4
 +  3  7  I  9
 _____
```

6.
```
    3  I  0  8
 +  3  0  9  5
 _____
```

7.
```
    2  4  5  5
 +  5  5  8  5
 _____
```

8.
```
    4  6  6  4
 +  I  3  4  3
 _____
```

q.
```
    I  7  2  7
 +  7  7  3  2
 _____
```

I0.
```
    3  8  4  I
 +  5  7  2  4
 _____
```

II.
```
    2  9  I  I
 +  7  5  4  8
 _____
```

I2.
```
    6  0  3  9
 +  5  4  0  6
 _____
```

Name _____

Adding 4-digit numbers

4134   2976   1795   3854   3256   2145

> Find the two star numbers that make each addition correct.

1.
```
  5 0 0 0
  2 9 7 6
+ 1 7 9 5
─────────
  4 7 7 1
```

2.
```
  6 0 0 0
_ _ _ _
+ _ _ _ _
─────────
  5 9 9 9
```

3.
```
  6 0 0 0
_ _ _ _
+ _ _ _ _
─────────
  5 9 2 9
```

4.
```
  7 0 0 0
_ _ _ _
+ _ _ _ _
─────────
  7 3 9 0
```

5.
```
  5 0 0 0
_ _ _ _
+ _ _ _ _
─────────
  5 4 0 1
```

6.
```
  7 0 0 0
_ _ _ _
+ _ _ _ _
─────────
  7 1 1 0
```

7.
```
  7 0 0 0
_ _ _ _
+ _ _ _ _
─────────
  6 8 3 0
```

8.
```
  7 0 0 0
_ _ _ _
+ _ _ _ _
─────────
  7 1 1 0
```

9.
```
  8 0 0 0
_ _ _ _
+ _ _ _ _
─────────
  7 9 8 8
```

29

Adding 4-digit numbers

round 1

+

_____

_____

score [ ]

round 2

+

_____

_____

score [ ]

round 3

+

_____

_____

score [ ]

round 4

+

_____

_____

score [ ]

Total score [ ]

Teacher's instructions
A game for two or more players, each with a copy of this scoresheet. Throw the dice eight times in each round. After each throw, all the players write the number in one of their boxes. After the eighth throw, the players add their numbers (checking each other's work). The player closest to 8000 scores 5 points, the next closest 4 points, and so on. The winner is the one with most points after four rounds.

Materials
A dice

Name _____

Sequences

Complete each sequence.

1.
   0 25 50 75

2.
   50 100 150

3.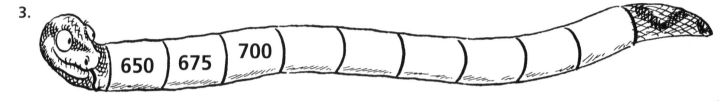
   650 675 700

4.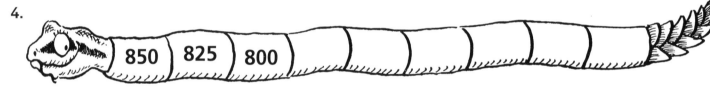
   850 825 800

5.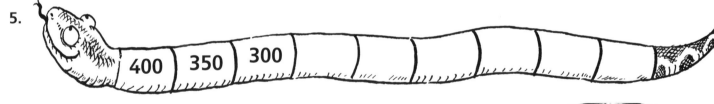
   400 350 300

6.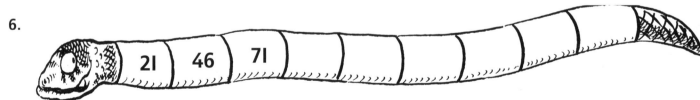
   21 46 71

7.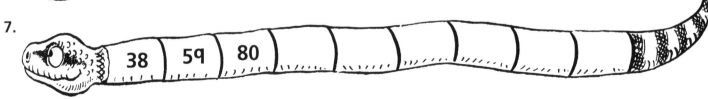
   38 59 80

8.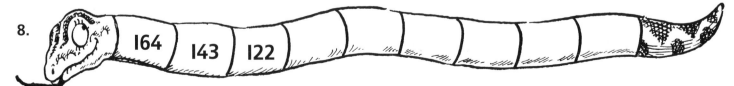
   164 143 122

Name _____

Position

Write the position of each balloon.

1.

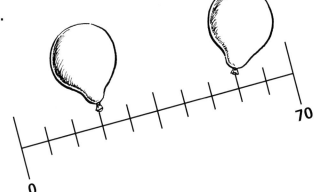

2.

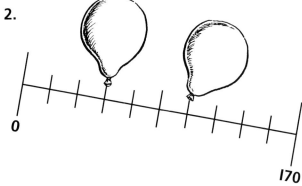

3.

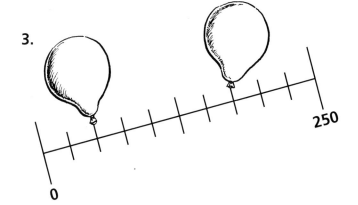

4.

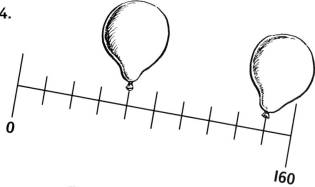

5.

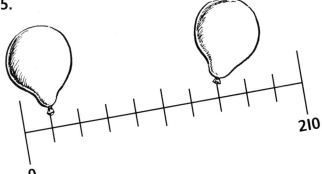

6.

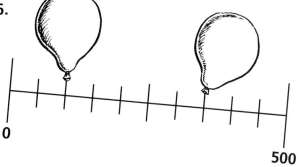

7.

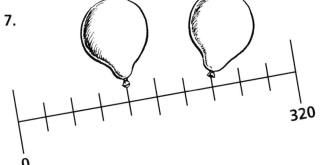

8.

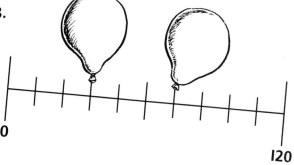

Name _____

Multiples

Use one colour to colour all the multiples of 3. Use another colour to colour all the multiples of 4.

Which numbers have been coloured twice?

1	2	3	4	5	6	7	8	9	10
11	12	13	14	15	16	17	18	19	20
21	22	23	24	25	26	27	28	29	30
31	32	33	34	35	36	37	38	39	40
41	42	43	44	45	46	47	48	49	50
51	52	53	54	55	56	57	58	59	60
61	62	63	64	65	66	67	68	69	70
71	72	73	74	75	76	77	78	79	80
81	82	83	84	85	86	87	88	89	90
91	92	93	94	95	96	97	98	99	100

What happens if you colour a different pair of multiples?

Name _____

Mystery numbers

Solve the clues to find the mystery numbers.

1.

Smallest common
multiple of 3 and 4.

2.

Smallest common
multiple of 5 and 7.

3.

Smallest common
multiple of 3 and 9.

4.

Multiple of 3.
Multiple of 4.
Between 20 and 25.

5.

Multiple of 4.
Multiple of 5.
Between 50 and 75.

6.

Multiple of 2.
Multiple of 5.
Between 25 and 40.

7.

Common multiple of
3 and 5.
Odd.
More than 20.
Less than 60.

8.

Common multiple of
3 and 7.
Odd.
Not 21.
Less than 100.

9.

Common multiple of
3 and 4.
Digit total 9.
Less than 50.

10.

Common multiple of
2, 3 and 4.
Less than 20.

11.

Common multiple of 3,
4 and 5.
Less than 100.

12.

Common multiple of
2, 4 and 8.
More than 40.
Less than 55.

Name _____

Multiplying by 100

Write how many centimetres
long each rope is.

I m = 100 cm

I.

21 m

[   ] cm

2.
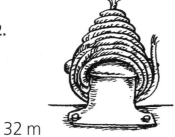

32 m

[   ] cm

3.
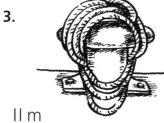

II m

[   ] cm

4.
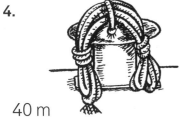

40 m

[   ] cm

5.
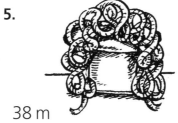

38 m

[   ] cm

6.
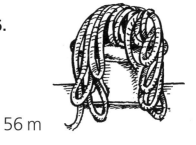

56 m

[   ] cm

7.

9 m

[   ] cm

8.
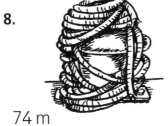

74 m

[   ] cm

q.

22 m

[   ] cm

Name _____

Multiplying by 10 and 100

> Write the missing numbers.

1. 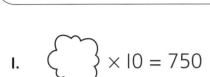 × 10 = 750

2. ⟨ ⟩ × 100 = 420

3. ⟨ ⟩ × 100 = 3200

4. 560 × ⟨ ⟩ = 5600

5. 8300 ÷ ⟨ ⟩ = 830

6. ⟨ ⟩ ÷ 100 = 49

7. 2700 ÷ ⟨ ⟩ = 27

8. 350 ÷ 10 = ⟨ ⟩

9. 35 × 100 = ⟨ ⟩

10. ⟨ ⟩ ÷ 100 = 0·35

11. ⟨ ⟩ × 10 = 17

12. 1·7 ÷ ⟨ ⟩ = 0·17

13. ⟨ ⟩ ÷ 100 = 0·91

14. ⟨ ⟩ × 10 = 6

15. 8 ÷ 10 = ⟨ ⟩

16. ⟨ ⟩ × 100 = 15

17. ⟨ ⟩ × 10 = 27

18. ⟨ ⟩ × 100 = 350

36

Name _____

Problem page

I. Caroline has a photo album that can fit 10 photos on each page. The album has 48 pages, but the first and last pages are already full. How many more photos can Caroline put in the album?

2. A mystery number is between 30 and 40. It is a common multiple of 3 and 4. What is the number?

3. Milk bottle crates hold 4 rows of 3 bottles. A milk truck has 10 full crates and 1 half-full crate to deliver. How many bottles are there to deliver?

4. Which common multiple of 4 and 5 is also a multiple of 15?

5. Picture hooks cost 14p each, or £10 for a pack of 100. The art gallery needs 200 picture hooks. How much will it save by buying packs of 100 instead of buying them separately?

6. Two mystery 1-digit numbers have 28 and 14 as common multiples. One mystery number is odd and the other is even. What other common multiple less than 50 do they have?

7. Niamh and Tim went to the bank. Niamh paid in £7·20 in 10p coins. Tim paid in £11·60 in 20p coins. Who paid in the most coins? How many more did they have?

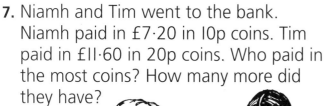
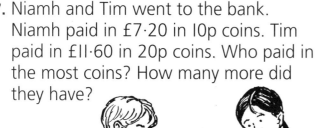

8. Which number between 30 and 60 is a common multiple of 3, 4 and 8?

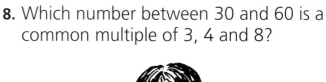

Multiplying by doubling and halving

Complete:

1. 4 × 35

= 2 × 🌧

= 🌧

2. 4 × 27

= 2 × 🌧

= 🌧

3. 4 × £3·50

= 2 × 🌧

= 🌧

4. 8 × 23

= 4 × 🌧

= 2 × 🌧

= 🌧

5. 8 × 36

= 4 × 🌧

= 2 × 🌧

= 🌧

6. 8 × £5·25

= 4 × 🌧

= 2 × 🌧

= 🌧

7. 16 × 17

= 8 × 🌧

= 4 × 🌧

= 2 × 🌧

= 🌧

8. 16 × 43

= 8 × 🌧

= 4 × 🌧

= 2 × 🌧

= 🌧

9. 16 × £4·20

= 8 × 🌧

= 4 × 🌧

= 2 × 🌧

= 🌧

Name _____

Multiplying by doubling

$14 \times 26 = 364$

$28 \times 36 = 1008$

$15 \times 38 = 570$

$270 \times 14 = 3780$

$36 \times 24 = 864$

$32 \times 18 = 576$

$52 \times 17 = 884$

$28 \times 35 = 980$

Use the multiplications above to complete these.

1. $14 \times 52 = $ _____

2. $30 \times 38 = $ _____

3. $14 \times 36 = $ _____

4. $7 \times 26 = $ _____

5. $36 \times 48 = $ _____

6. $270 \times 28 = $ _____

7. $15 \times 19 = $ _____

8. $135 \times 14 = $ _____

9. $28 \times 72 = $ _____

10. $32 \times 36 = $ _____

11. $16 \times 18 = $ _____

12. $36 \times 12 = $ _____

13. $52 \times 34 = $ _____

14. $28 \times 70 = $ _____

15. $14 \times 35 = $ _____

16. $26 \times 17 = $ _____

Name _____

Multiplying by 25, 50 and 100

  (62 × 5) (11 × 50) (24 × 5) (32 × 50) (44 × 5) (32 × 50)

  (22 × 50) (46 × 5) (17 × 50) (31 × 5) (46 × 50) (17 × 5)

  (42 × 50) (35 × 50) (11 × 25) (42 × 5) (24 × 50) (23 × 5)

  (36 × 50) (84 × 5) (23 × 25) (16 × 50) (48 × 5) (38 × 50)

  (32 × 25) (55 × 5) (30 × 50) (58 × 50) (86 × 5) (28 × 50)

  (26 × 5) (44 × 50) (66 × 5) (34 × 50) (18 × 25) (82 × 5)

Teacher's instructions
A game for 2 players. Take turns to throw the two dice and choose a multiplication
to match the throws (row and column). Say the answer by working it out in your
head. Check each other's answers. If correct place one of your counters
on the spot.
The winner is the first to have 4 counters in any straight line.

Materials
2 dice
Set of counters each of
your own colour

40

Multiplying

120	6	40	250	90	180
240	200	60	3	40	120
100	30	180	150	100	5
60	160	300	20	80	120
240	4	120	2	200	60
80	300	50	360	150	120

Teacher's instructions
A game for two players.
Take turns to throw the dice, and say a multiplication using the dice number. If
the answer appears on the board, cover it with a counter. For example, if you
throw a '3' you can say 'Three twenties are sixty', and place a counter on '60'.
Check each other's answers. The winner is the first to put three of their counters
in a straight line.

41

Materials
A dice
Set of counters
each

Name _____

Multiplying

1. ☐ × 40 = _____

2. ☐ × 20 = _____

3. ☐ × 200 = _____

4. ☐ × 400 = _____

5. ☐ × 60 = _____

6. ☐ × 300 = _____

7. ☐ × 80 = _____

8. ☐ × 500 = _____

9. ☐ × 90 = _____

10. ☐ × 700 = _____

11. ☐ × 70 = _____

12. ☐ × 30 = _____

13. ☐ × 80 = _____

14. ☐ × 600 = _____

15. ☐ × 90 = _____

16. ☐ × 500 = _____

17. ☐ × 400 = _____

18. ☐ × 60 = _____

19. ☐ × 800 = _____

20. ☐ × 40 = _____

Teacher's instructions
Shuffle the cards. Start with the left column. Deal them out, one at a time, and write the matching number in the spaces, then multiply. Reshuffle the cards and repeat for the right column.

Materials
Number cards (1 to 10)

Name _____

Multiplying

Roll a dice to find the multiplying number each time, then multiply.

If you roll a 'I', then roll again.

I. ☐ × 32 = (× 30) + (× 2)

= _____ + _____ = _____

2. ☐ × 27 = (× 20) + (× 7)

= _____ + _____ = _____

3. ☐ × 45 = ( ) + ( )

= _____ + _____ = _____

4. ☐ × 18 = ( ) + ( )

= _____ + _____ = _____

5. ☐ × 38 = ( ) + ( )

= _____ + _____ = _____

6. ☐ × 56 = ( ) + ( )

= _____ + _____ = _____

Four in a line

72	120	180	85	126
140	68	78	192	98
99	198	252	96	66
60	186	138	132	76
86	396	168	228	44

6 × 33 3 × 46 2 × 22 2 × 34 30 × 6
3 × 26 3 × 76 3 × 22 3 × 62
20 × 3 4 × 19
2 × 36 2 × 66
3 × 56 6 × 66
5 × 28 6 × 42
2 × 43 5 × 17
2 × 49 60 × 2
6 × 32 2 × 48 3 × 33 6 × 23

Name _____

Teacher's instructions
A game for two players.
Take turns to choose a multiplication and work out the answer. If the answer appears on the board, cover it with one of your counters. The winner is the first to have four counters in any straight line.

Materials
A set of counters each

44

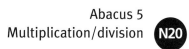

Name _____

Halves and quarters

Complete.

1. $\frac{1}{2}$ of £44 = ⬡ ➡ $\frac{1}{4}$ of £44 = ⬡

2. $\frac{1}{2}$ of £56 = ⬡ ➡ $\frac{1}{4}$ of £56 = ⬡

3. $\frac{1}{2}$ of £72 = ⬡ ➡ $\frac{1}{4}$ of £72 = ⬡

4. $\frac{1}{2}$ of £36 = ⬡ ➡ $\frac{1}{4}$ of £36 = ⬡

5. $\frac{1}{2}$ of £124 = ⬡ ➡ $\frac{1}{4}$ of £124 = ⬡

6. $\frac{1}{2}$ of £136 = ⬡ ➡ $\frac{1}{4}$ of £136 = ⬡

7. $\frac{1}{2}$ of £108 = ⬡ ➡ $\frac{1}{4}$ of £108 = ⬡

8. $\frac{1}{2}$ of £84 = ⬡ ➡ $\frac{1}{4}$ of £84 = ⬡

9. $\frac{1}{2}$ of £96 = ⬡ ➡ $\frac{1}{4}$ of £96 = ⬡

10. $\frac{1}{2}$ of £288 = ⬡ ➡ $\frac{1}{4}$ of £288 = ⬡

45

Dividing by 2, 4 or 8

  136    102    92    392

  296   60    328   110

  42    152    424    124

  54    344    156    232

  488    188    200    70

  90    264    236    456

Teacher's instructions
A game for 2 players.
Take turns to throw the dice. Choose any number in the matching row. If the number divides exactly by 2 collect 1 cube, exactly by 4 collect 2 cubes, exactly by 8 collect 3 cubes. Check each other's calculation. Place a counter on the number, so it can't be used again. The winner is the first to collect 25 cubes.

Materials
Cubes
2 dice

46

Name _____

Hundredths

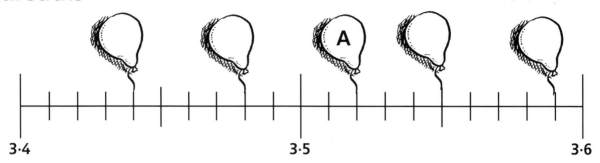

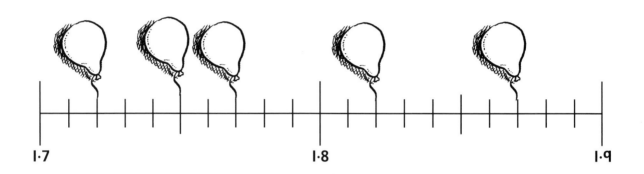

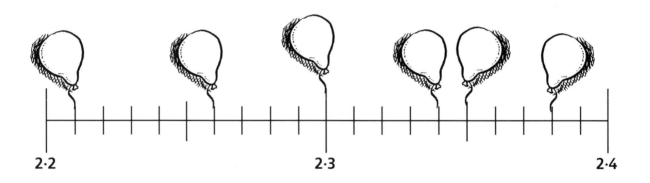

> Write the correct letter for each balloon.

A	3·52	B	1·77	C	1·72	D	2·38
E	1·82	F	3·48	G	2·34	H	3·44
I	2·35	J	2·26	K	3·55	L	1·75
M	3·59	N	2·3	P	1·87	Q	2·21

Name _____

Ordering decimals

Write < or > between each pair.

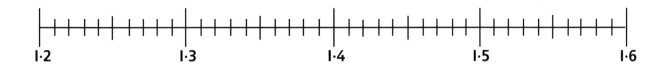

| 1·2 | 1·3 | 1·4 | 1·5 | 1·6 |

1. 1·25 ⟨⟩ 1·35

2. 1·41 ⟨⟩ 1·37

3   1·46 ⟨⟩ 1·57

4. 1·2 ⟨⟩ 1·4

5. 1·5 ⟨⟩ 1·3

6. 1·3 ⟨⟩ 1·42

7. 1·3 ⟨⟩ 1·24

8. 1·59 ⟨⟩ 1·5

9. 1·25 ⟨⟩ 1·3

10. 1·3 ⟨⟩ 1·29

11. 1·4 ⟨⟩ 1·61

12. 1·41 ⟨⟩ 1·3

13. 1·21 ⟨⟩ 1·5

14. 1·54 ⟨⟩ 1·35

15. $1\frac{31}{100}$ ⟨⟩ $1\frac{3}{10}$

16. 1·5 ⟨⟩ $1\frac{47}{100}$

17. 1·32 ⟨⟩ $1\frac{4}{10}$

18. $1\frac{41}{100}$ ⟨⟩ 1·45

19. 1·5 ⟨⟩ $1\frac{33}{100}$

20. $1\frac{3}{10}$ ⟨⟩ $1\frac{29}{100}$

48

Name _____

Ordering decimals

Write <, > or = between each pair.

1. $1 \cdot 3$ ⬡ $2\frac{4}{10}$

2. $2 \cdot 7$ ⬡ $1\frac{6}{10}$

3. $3 \cdot 4$ ⬡ $4 \cdot 7$

4. $1\frac{5}{10}$ ⬡ $2\frac{7}{10}$

5. $5\frac{8}{10}$ ⬡ $3 \cdot 5$

6. $4\frac{1}{10}$ ⬡ $1 \cdot 4$

7. $5\frac{7}{10}$ ⬡ $7 \cdot 5$

8. $2 \cdot 3$ ⬡ $\frac{23}{10}$

9. $1 \cdot 5$ ⬡ $1\frac{1}{10}$

10. $2 \cdot 6$ ⬡ $2\frac{3}{10}$

11. $3\frac{4}{10}$ ⬡ $3\frac{37}{100}$

12. $5 \cdot 41$ ⬡ $5\frac{36}{100}$

13. $2\frac{6}{10}$ ⬡ $2 \cdot 45$

14. $\frac{4}{100}$ ⬡ $0 \cdot 03$

15. $0 \cdot 5$ ⬡ $\frac{50}{100}$

16. $0 \cdot 60$ ⬡ $\frac{6}{10}$

17. $3\frac{2}{10}$ ⬡ $0 \cdot 3$

18. $5 \cdot 45$ ⬡ $5\frac{5}{10}$

Name _____

Matching fractions and decimals

Use the digits in each set to make matching fractions and decimals.

1. { 0 1 5 2 } $\dfrac{1}{2}$ = 0 . 5

2. { 7 7 0 10 } $\dfrac{\square}{\square}$ = □ . □

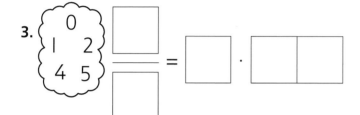

3. { 0 1 2 4 5 } $\dfrac{\square}{\square}$ = □ . □□

4. { 4 8 0 2 } $\dfrac{\square}{\square}$ = □ . □

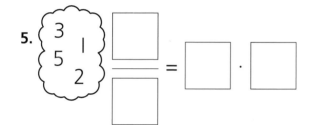

5. { 3 1 5 2 } $\dfrac{\square}{\square}$ = □ . □

6. { 0 3 4 5 7 } $\dfrac{\square}{\square}$ = □ . □□

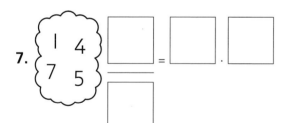

7. { 1 4 7 5 } $\dfrac{\square}{\square}$ = □ . □

8. { 3 5 6 0 } $\dfrac{\square}{\square}$ = □ . □

9. { 4 5 8 0 } $\dfrac{\square}{\square}$ = □ . □

10. { 5 4 0 8 } $\dfrac{\square}{\square}$ = □ . □

11. { 0 9 3 3 } $\dfrac{\square}{\square}$ = □ . □

12. { 6 1 8 5 } $\dfrac{\square}{\square}$ = □ . □

Name _____

Problem page

1. The school magazine had 1000 copies to sell. 16 children each sold thirty-five magazines. How many magazines are left to be sold?

2. Elmo the cat eats 1 tin of catfood every day. A tin costs 25p. How much does it cost to feed Elmo for 4 weeks?

3. Andrea gets £4·50 each week for washing her dad's car. How much does she earn in a year?

4. Ali earns £1·50 an hour for baby-sitting. Last month he baby-sat for 4 hours on each of 4 Saturdays, and for 3 hours on 2 Fridays. How much did he earn in the month?

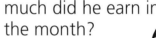

5. Jon had saved £12·48. He earned £3·65 an hour for 3 hours gardening. How much does he have now? How much more does he need to have saved £30?

6. Sonia had £36 in her bank. She gave $\frac{1}{4}$ of her savings to a charity, and spent $\frac{1}{3}$ of her savings on presents. How much has she left in the bank?

7. Ben ate $\frac{3}{8}$ of his pizza, and gave $\frac{1}{4}$ to each of Safa and Danny. What fraction of the pizza is left?

8. Tickets to the concert cost £4·50 for adults and are half-price for children. How much change will a group of two adults and three children get from £20?

Name _____

Adding and subtracting

Complete these.

1. $69 + 30 =$ _____

2. $89 - 50 =$ _____

3. $326 + 40 =$ _____

4. $375 - 60 =$ _____

5. $329 - 50 =$ _____

6. $268 + 70 =$ _____

7. $532 + 200 =$ _____

8. $465 - 300 =$ _____

9. $751 - 600 =$ _____

10. $632 + 800 =$ _____

11. $527 + 30 =$ _____

12. $756 - 40 =$ _____

13. $287 - 90 =$ _____

14. $385 + 90 =$ _____

15. $1540 - 700 =$ _____

16. $380 + 1200 =$ _____

Name _____

Adding and subtracting

Write the missing numbers.

1. $450 + \boxed{} = 520$

2. $630 - \boxed{} = 550$

3. $\boxed{} + 80 = 240$

4. $\boxed{} - 60 = 460$

5. $320 + \boxed{} = 390$

6. $780 - \boxed{} = 730$

7. $\boxed{} + 300 = 730$

8. $590 - \boxed{} = 390$

9. $680 + \boxed{} = 1380$

10. $\boxed{} - 800 = 620$

11. $\boxed{} + 900 = 1390$

12. $1050 - \boxed{} = 350$

13. $90 + \boxed{} = 160$

14. $\boxed{} - 80 = 150$

15. $380 + \boxed{} = 490$

16. $560 - \boxed{} = 310$

Name _____

Adding and subtracting

Complete these.

1. $142 + 99 = $ _____

2. $365 - 98 = $ _____

3. $274 + 198 = $ _____

4. $520 - 102 = $ _____

5. $352 + 203 = $ _____

6. $486 - 199 = $ _____

7. $471 + 397 = $ _____

8. $370 - 201 = $ _____

9. $643 - 198 = $ _____

10. $432 + 296 = $ _____

11. $785 - 399 = $ _____

12. $514 + 499 = $ _____

13. $957 - 296 = $ _____

14. $648 + 197 = $ _____

15. $560 + 90 = $ _____

16. $750 + 90 = $ _____

17. $732 + 104 = $ _____

18. $260 - 101 = $ _____

19. $854 - 603 = $ _____

20. $472 + 999 = $ _____

Name _____

Differences

Write the difference between the numbers.

1.

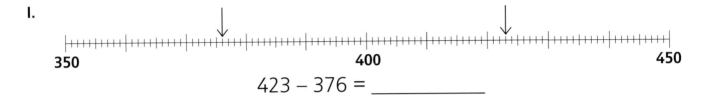

$$423 - 376 = \underline{\hphantom{xxxxxx}}$$

2.

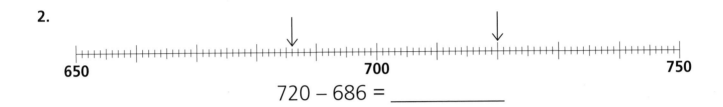

$$720 - 686 = \underline{\hphantom{xxxxxx}}$$

3.

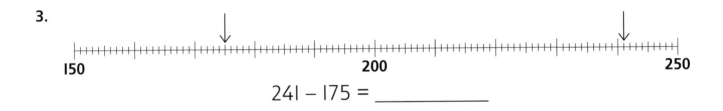

$$241 - 175 = \underline{\hphantom{xxxxxx}}$$

4.

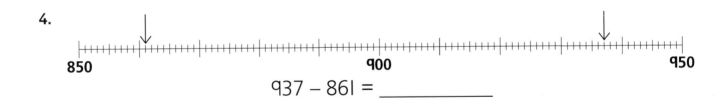

$$937 - 861 = \underline{\hphantom{xxxxxx}}$$

5.

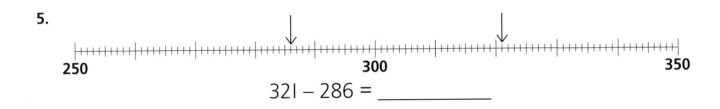

$$321 - 286 = \underline{\hphantom{xxxxxx}}$$

6.

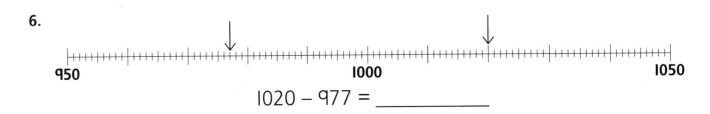

$$1020 - 977 = \underline{\hphantom{xxxxxx}}$$

Name _____

Subtracting

Complete these.

I. 781 – 698 = _____

2. 965 – 597 = _____

3. 932 – 495 = _____

4. 873 – 299 = _____

5. 2004 – 1997 = _____

6. 4002 – 2995 = _____

7. 6005 – 3996 = _____

8. 7010 – 4999 = _____

9. 8015 – 1999 = _____

10. 9024 – 2997 = _____

II. 1020 – 899 = _____

12. 1430 – 799 = _____

13. 2084 – 1995 = _____

14. 9641 – 3995 = _____

15. 6026 – 3980 = _____

16. 5840 – 2970 = _____

17. 7152 – 4960 = _____

18. 7532 – 5990 = _____

Name _____

Subtracting

Complete these.

I.
```
    5   7   3   2
–       4   6   4
_____
```

2.
```
    6   4   5   6
–       5   4   2
_____
```

3.
```
    7   8   3   2
–       1   7   9
_____
```

4.
```
    4   8   5   1
–       7   4   2
_____
```

5.
```
    8   3   6   9
–       1   8   6
_____
```

6.
```
    6   2   7   5
–       9   3   2
_____
```

7.
```
    3   0   3   4
–       4   7   5
_____
```

8.
```
    7   5   1   7
–       6   2   5
_____
```

9.
```
    5   7   8   8
–       8   3   6
_____
```

10.
```
    9   8   2   6
–       5   4   9
_____
```

II.
```
    4   6   3   6
–       7   2   3
_____
```

12.
```
    9   4   9   2
–       6   0   8
_____
```

Name _____

Subtracting

In each subtraction, throw three dice to make a 3-digit number.

Write it and take away.

3 dice

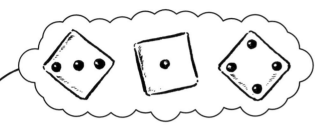

1. (7 4 0 0)

```
  7 6 9 8
-   3 1 4
─────────
  7 3 8 4
─────────
```

2. ( )

```
  6 8 9 7
-
─────────
```

3. ( )

```
  7 6 6 8
-
─────────
```

4. ( )

```
  6 2 5 1
-
─────────
```

5. ( )

```
  4 3 7 8
-
─────────
```

6. ( )

```
  2 9 7 2
-
─────────
```

7. ( )

```
  5 2 8 6
-
─────────
```

8. ( )

```
  3 2 5 1
-
─────────
```

9. ( )

```
  4 0 7 3
-
─────────
```

Name _____

Subtracting

Choose your methods to subtract.

826   subtract

399 = _____

785 = _____

198 = _____

16 = _____

676 = _____

538   subtract

215 = _____

298 = _____

36 = _____

132 = _____

490 = _____

786   subtract

75 = _____

198 = _____

316 = _____

599 = _____

160 = _____

59

Name _____

Problem page

I. Frank will be 48 years old in the year 2009. His mother was 27 when he was born. In what year was his mother born? How old will she be in the year 2012?

2. A cruise ship has 476 passengers. At the first port 198 passengers visit the port whilst the others stay on the ship. Of those left on the ship 97 have lunch and the others sunbathe. How many passengers are sunbathing?

3. The Rattan family want to have a holiday in Florida. The travel agent is offering a holiday for four people for £2000. Mr Rattan uses the internet and finds that he can have the same holiday for £465 each. How much does the Rattan family save?

4. Rovers football stadium has 9620 seats. There are 3988 seats undercover. On Saturday the stadium is full. How many fans will get wet if it rains?

5. The snail race is 10 metres long. Sammy Snail travels 15 centimetres in the first minute, and 112 millimetres in the second minute. How much further must Sammy go?

6. A mystery number is 1988 less than 3465. How much less than 1500 is the number?

7. Two numbers have a total of 1175. One of the numbers is 876. What is the difference between the two numbers?

8. The Kirk family are choosing between a holiday to Egypt which costs £589 each and a holiday to Malaysia which costs £642 each. If 4 people are travelling, how much more will it cost to choose Malaysia instead of Egypt?

Name _____

Dividing by 2

Place a tick beside each number that can be divided exactly by 2.

I. | 57 |

2. | 72 |

3. | 46 |

4. | 31 |

5. | 90 |

6. | 45 |

7. | 32 |

8. | 50 |

9. | 17 |

10. | 148 |

II. | 259 |

12. | 307 |

Dividing by 4

Place a tick beside each number that can be divided exactly by 4.

13. | 48 |

14. | 62 |

15. | 78 |

16. | 144 |

17. | 50 |

18. | 94 |

19. | 438 |

20. | 350 |

21. | 460 |

22. | 720 |

23. | 136 |

24. | 84 |

Name _____

Division rules

Put ticks in the table to show which numbers divide exactly into the numbers on the left.

Write six numbers of your own and fill in the ticks.

Number	÷ 2	÷ 4	÷ 5	÷ 10	÷ 100
40					
150					
600					
84					
92					
112					
235					
500					
468					
225					

Name _____

Factors

Write numbers to make a different multiplication each time.

1. **6** (1) × (6) , (2) × (3)

2. **8** ( ) × ( ) , ( ) × ( )

3. **9** ( ) × ( ) , ( ) × ( )

4. **10** ( ) × ( ) , ( ) × ( )

5. **11** ( ) × ( )

6. **12** ( ) × ( ) , ( ) × ( ) , ( ) × ( )

7. **15** ( ) × ( ) , ( ) × ( )

8. **20** ( ) × ( ) , ( ) × ( ) , ( ) × ( )

9. **21** ( ) × ( ) , ( ) × ( )

10. **22** ( ) × ( ) , ( ) × ( )

11. **24** ( ) × ( ) , ( ) × ( ) ,
    ( ) × ( ) , ( ) × ( )

12. **25** ( ) × ( ) , ( ) × ( )

Name _____

Factors

Complete the list of factors.

41	1, 41
42	1, 2, 3, 6, 7, 14, 21, 42
43	
44	
45	
46	
47	
48	
49	
50	
51	
52	
53	
54	
55	
56	
57	
58	
59	
60	

Problem page

I. Julia saves 50p coins and Phil saves 20p coins. Julia has saved 26 coins. Phil has saved 67 coins. Who has saved the most, and by how much?

2. A rectangle has a perimeter of 28 centimetres. One side is 6 cm long. What is its area?

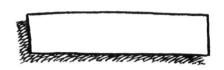

3. You can choose between a bag of thirty £2 coins, a bag of one hundred and twenty-two 50p coins, or a bag of three hundred and ten 20p coins. Which holds the most money? Which holds the least?

4. Six numbers are factors of 18. Three of them are odd and three are even. Two of the odd factors are I and 3. Which is the third? Two of the even factors are 2 and 18. Which is the third?

5. The Lewis family went to France. In France they hired a car and travelled 240 km. If 5 miles is approximately 8 km, how many miles did they travel?

6. Which pair of factors of 24 differs by 5? Which pair has a total of 10?

7. The area of a rectangle is 45 square centimetres. The shorter sides of the rectangle are 5 centimetres long. How much longer are the longer sides? What is the perimeter of the rectangle?

8. A mystery number less than 20 has four factors. Three of its factors are consecutive odd numbers. What is the number?

Name _____

Negative numbers

Write the temperature at each city.

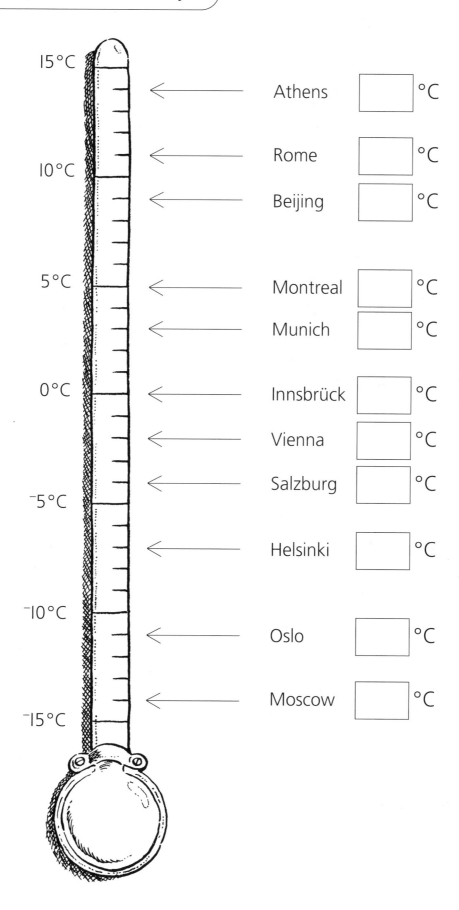

Athens		°C
Rome		°C
Beijing		°C
Montreal		°C
Munich		°C
Innsbrück		°C
Vienna		°C
Salzburg		°C
Helsinki		°C
Oslo		°C
Moscow		°C

Name _____

Negative numbers

Write < or > between each pair.

1. 3 ⟨ ⟩ 7

2. ⁻2 ⟨ ⟩ 4

3. 5 ⟨ ⟩ ⁻3

4. ⁻3 ⟨ ⟩ ⁻5

5. 2 ⟨ ⟩ 6

6. 7 ⟨ ⟩ 4

7. ⁻7 ⟨ ⟩ ⁻3

8. 7 ⟨ ⟩ ⁻4

9. 8 ⟨ ⟩ ⁻3

10. ⁻2 ⟨ ⟩ ⁻1

11. 0 ⟨ ⟩ ⁻3

12. 2 ⟨ ⟩ ⁻1

13. ⁻3 ⟨ ⟩ 5

14. 5 ⟨ ⟩ 0

15. ⁻4 ⟨ ⟩ 0

16. 4 ⟨ ⟩ ⁻2

17. ⁻1 ⟨ ⟩ ⁻3

18. 0 ⟨ ⟩ ⁻6

Name _____

Jumping

Each set of jumps starts at 0.
Write the missing numbers.

finish **finish**

1. up 4 down 5 [ ]   2. up 2 up 4 [ ]

3. up 3 down 6 [ ]   4. up 6 down 9 [ ]

5. down 2 down 5 [ ]   6. down 7 up 3 [ ]

7. _____ down 2 [6]   8. _____ up 3 [5]

9. _____ up 4 [⁻3]   10. _____ down 2 [⁻3]

11. _____ down 3 [2]   12. _____ down 8 [1]

13. _____ down 5 [⁻1]   14. _____ up 7 [⁻1]

15. up 2 _____ [0]   16. down 3 _____ [⁻6]

17. down 6 _____ [2]   18. up 8 _____ [⁻1]

19. up 5 _____ [⁻3]   20. down 7 _____ [4]

21. down 3 _____ [⁻2]   22. up 2 _____ [⁻5]

10

5

0

⁻5

⁻10

68

Name _____

Multiplying

Roll a dice to find the multiplying number each time, then multiply.

If you roll a 'I', roll again.

A dice

I. ⬭

```
    1  3  5
        ┌───┐
 X      │ 3 │
        └───┘
 ──────────────
    3  0  0
    9  0
    1  5
 ──────────────
```

2. ⬭

```
    2  1  4
        ┌───┐
 X      │   │
        └───┘
 ──────────────
```

3. ⬭

```
    1  6  7
        ┌───┐
 X      │   │
        └───┘
 ──────────────
```

4. ⬭

```
    3  2  1
        ┌───┐
 X      │   │
        └───┘
 ──────────────
```

5. ⬭

```
    4  5  3
        ┌───┐
 X      │   │
        └───┘
 ──────────────
```

6. ⬭

```
    6  1  7
        ┌───┐
 X      │   │
        └───┘
 ──────────────
```

7. ⬭

```
    2  8  9
        ┌───┐
 X      │   │
        └───┘
 ──────────────
```

8. ⬭

```
    1  9  6
        ┌───┐
 X      │   │
        └───┘
 ──────────────
```

q. ⬭

```
    4  0  8
        ┌───┐
 X      │   │
        └───┘
 ──────────────
```

Name _____

Multiplying

> Find the area of each rectangle by splitting it up into smaller rectangles. Write the area of each, then add to find the total.

I. 17 cm × 24 cm = $\underline{408}$ cm^2

	20	4
10	200	40
7	140	28

```
 200
 140
  40
+ 28
 408
  1
```

2. 16 cm × 21 cm = _____

3. 22 cm × 31 cm = _____

4. 14 cm × 26 cm = _____

5. 22 cm × 43 cm = _____

6. 18 cm × 32 cm = _____

Name _____

Multiplying

Complete these.

I.
```
      5   8
  x   2   3
  _____
```

2.
```
      2   6
  x   I   9
  _____
```

3.
```
      4   5
  x   2   7
  _____
```

4.
```
      2   7
  x   3   I
  _____
```

5.
```
      4   6
  x   I   8
  _____
```

6.
```
      3   5
  x   2   9
  _____
```

7.
```
      I   7
  x   3   8
  _____
```

8.
```
      4   6
  x   4   6
  _____
```

q.
```
      2   8
  x   I   5
  _____
```

Name _____

Multiplying

round 1

X

_____ score

_____

round 2

X

_____ score

_____

round 3

X

_____ score

_____

round 4

X

_____ score

_____

Total score

Teacher's instructions
A game for two or more players, each with a copy of this scoresheet.
Throw the dice four times in each round. After each throw, all the players write the number in one of their boxes. After the fourth throw the players multiply the numbers together. Check each other's multiplications, using a calculator if necessary. The player with the largest answer scores 4 points, the next largest 3 points, and so on. The winner is the one with the most points after four rounds.

Materials
A dice
A calculator (optional)

72

Name _____

Multiplying

> Find the area of each rectangle by splitting it up into smaller rectangles. Write the area of each, then add to find the total.

I. $6\,cm \times 2 \cdot 6\,cm = \underline{15 \cdot 6\,cm^2}$

$$6 \times 2 \cdot 6 = 6 \times 2 \cdot 0 = \quad 12 \cdot 0$$
$$6 \times 0 \cdot 6 = \quad \underline{3 \cdot 6}$$
$$\underline{15 \cdot 6}\,cm^2$$

2. $9\,cm \times 3 \cdot 7\,cm = \underline{}$

3. $7\,cm \times 4 \cdot 1\,cm = \underline{}$

4. $8\,cm \times 2 \cdot 8\,cm = \underline{}$

5. $6\,cm \times 3 \cdot 3\,cm = \underline{}$

6. $5\,cm \times 2 \cdot 9\,cm = \underline{}$

Name _____

Multiplying

Estimate, then multiply.

1.

$3 \times 5 \cdot 6$

$3 \times 5 \cdot 0 =$

$3 \times 0 \cdot 6 =$

$3 \times 5 \cdot 6 =$

2.

$2 \times 7 \cdot 8$

$2 \times 7 \cdot 0 =$

$2 \times 0 \cdot 8 =$

$2 \times 7 \cdot 8 =$

3.

$5 \times 4 \cdot 9$

$5 \times 4 \cdot 0 =$

$5 \times 0 \cdot 9 =$

$5 \times 4 \cdot 9 =$

4.

$6 \times 3 \cdot 7$

$6 \times \quad =$

$6 \times \quad =$

$6 \times \quad =$

5.

$4 \times 2 \cdot 8$

$4 \times \quad =$

$4 \times \quad =$

$4 \times \quad =$

6.

$7 \times 5 \cdot 4$

$7 \times \quad =$

$7 \times \quad =$

$7 \times \quad =$

7.

$3 \times 12 \cdot 4$

$3 \times \quad =$

$3 \times \quad =$

$3 \times \quad =$

8.

$8 \times 10 \cdot 7$

$8 \times \quad =$

$8 \times \quad =$

$8 \times \quad =$

9.

$6 \times 9 \cdot 6$

$6 \times \quad =$

$6 \times \quad =$

$6 \times \quad =$

Name _____

Multiplying

> Cut out these multiplication cards.
> Put them in order of your estimated answers, smallest to largest.
> Then do the multiplications to see if your order was correct.

3 x 3·7	**5 x 4·2**	**6 x 1·9**	**7 x 2·8**
3 x 3·0 =	=	=	=
3 x 0·7 =	=	=	=
3 x 3·7 = ⟨⟩	= ⟨⟩	= ⟨⟩	= ⟨⟩
5 x 3·2	**7 x 3·6**	**9 x 0·8**	**4 x 1·7**
=	=	=	=
=	=	=	=
= ⟨⟩	= ⟨⟩	= ⟨⟩	= ⟨⟩
5 x 1·8	**3 x 4·3**	**5 x 3·5**	**6 x 1·8**
=	=	=	=
=	=	=	=
= ⟨⟩	= ⟨⟩	= ⟨⟩	= ⟨⟩
3 x 2·6	**2 x 7·3**	**4 x 4·5**	**6 x 2·3**
=	=	=	=
=	=	=	=
= ⟨⟩	= ⟨⟩	= ⟨⟩	= ⟨⟩

Name _____

Dividing

Estimate, then divide.

---

1. $67 \div 3 =$ _22 r 1_

$\boxed{20}$

$$3\overline{)67}$$
$$-\ 60 \qquad 20 \times 3$$
$$\overline{7}$$
$$-\ 6 \qquad 2 \times 3$$
$$\overline{1}$$

---

2. $93 \div 4 =$ _____

$\bigcirc$

$$4\overline{)93}$$

---

3. $89 \div 5 =$ _____

$\bigcirc$

$$5\overline{)89}$$

---

4. $74 \div 6 =$ _____

$\bigcirc$

$$6\overline{)7}$$

---

5. $95 \div 3 =$ _____

$\bigcirc$

$$3\overline{)95}$$

---

6. $67 \div 4 =$ _____

$\bigcirc$

$$4\overline{)67}$$

---

7. $116 \div 5 =$ _____

$\bigcirc$

$$5\overline{)116}$$

---

8. $99 \div 7 =$ _____

$\bigcirc$

$$7\overline{)99}$$

---

9. $107 \div 6 =$ _____

$\bigcirc$

$$6\overline{)107}$$

Name _____

Dividing

Throw a dice to find the dividing number.
If you throw a 'I' then throw again.

Estimate, then divide.

A dice

I. **507 ÷** ☐ **=** _____

$$\overline{)507}$$

2. **289 ÷** ☐ **=** _____

$$\overline{)289}$$

3. **176 ÷** ☐ **=** _____

$$\overline{)176}$$

4. **465 ÷** ☐ **=** _____

$$\overline{)465}$$

5. **615 ÷** ☐ **=** _____

$$\overline{)615}$$

6. **732 ÷** ☐ **=** _____

$$\overline{)732}$$

Name _____

Problem page

I. The temperature in the classroom was I4 °C at 8 o'clock in the morning. It rose by 5 °C in the afternoon, then fell 8 °C by 7 o'clock in the evening. What was the temperature then?

2. A mystery number is negative. It is 4 more than the number that is 2 less than ⁻3. What is the number?

3. The distance from Clare's house to London is I43 miles. How far does she travel in two return trips?

4. A return flight to Jersey costs £I86. A hotel costs £42 per person per night. What is the cost of a 3-day break for 3 people?

5. The length of a side of a regular pentagon is 4·2 cm. What is its perimeter?

6. The perimeter of a regular hexagon is I9·2 cm. What is the length of each side of the hexagon?

7. 750 people are queuing to buy tickets for a concert. The concert hall has I6 rows of 4I seats. How many of the people queuing will not get a ticket?

8. Fairfield School magazine costs I8p. Last week 34 copies were sold. The week before 28 copies were sold. How much money has the school raised from the magazine in the last two weeks?

Name _____

Dividing

Divide 87 by all the numbers
from 2 to 10. Estimate first.

1.

$2\overline{)8\ 7}$

2.

$3\overline{)8\ 7}$

3.

$4\overline{)8\ 7}$

4.

$5\overline{)8\ 7}$

5.

$6\overline{)8\ 7}$

6.

$7\overline{)8\ 7}$

7.

$8\overline{)8\ 7}$

8.

$9\overline{)8\ 7}$

9.

$10\overline{)8\ 7}$

Choose your own number between 50 and
100. Divide by all the numbers from 2 to 10.

Name _____

Dividing

Estimate, then divide.

I. (⬭)

7⟌1 5 2

2. (⬭)

3⟌1 0 9

3. (⬭)

5⟌2 6 1

4. (⬭)

8⟌1 8 7

5. (⬭)

4⟌1 5 6

6. (⬭)

7⟌2 2 3

7. (⬭)

9⟌2 5 4

8. (⬭)

6⟌1 7 8

q. (⬭)

8⟌2 1 3

Name _____

Rounding decimals

Write the position of each pointer. Round the decimal number to its nearest whole number.

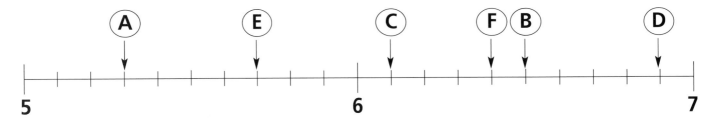

A: <u>5·3 ———→ 5</u>   B: _____

C: _____   D: _____

E: _____   F: _____

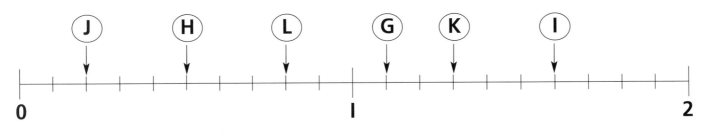

G: _____   H: _____

I: _____   J: _____

K: _____   L: _____

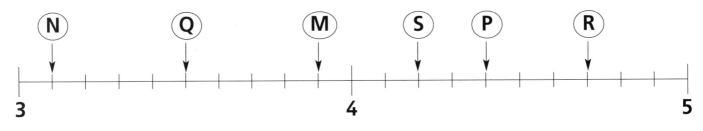

M: _____   N: _____

P: _____   Q: _____

R: _____   S: _____

81

Name _____

Rounding to the nearest whole number

Choose two of these to make decimal numbers that round to these nearest whole numbers.

1. ☐ . ☐ ⟶ **5**

2. ☐ . ☐ ⟶ **4**

3. ☐ . ☐ ⟶ **8**

4. ☐ . ☐ ⟶ **7**

5. ☐ . ☐ ⟶ **2**

6. ☐ . ☐ ⟶ **1**

7. ☐ . ☐ ⟶ **9**

8. ☐ . ☐ ⟶ **10**

Now choose two of these.

9. ☐ . ☐ ⟶ **2**

10. ☐ . ☐ ⟶ **4**

11. ☐ . ☐ ⟶ **7**

12. ☐ . ☐ ⟶ **8**

13. ☐ . ☐ ⟶ **9**

14. ☐ . ☐ ⟶ **1**

15. ☐ . ☐ ⟶ **3**

16. ☐ . ☐ ⟶ **6**

Rounding to the nearest whole number

Round   **Score**

1   ▢▢ · ▢ ⟶ ▢▢   ☁

2   ▢▢ · ▢ ⟶ ▢▢   ☁

3   ▢▢ · ▢ ⟶ ▢▢   ☁

4   ▢▢ · ▢ ⟶ ▢▢   ☁

5   ▢▢ · ▢ ⟶ ▢▢   ☁

6   ▢▢ · ▢ ⟶ ▢▢   ☁

Total score ☁

Teacher's instructions
A game for two players, each with a copy of this scoresheet. Play round 1. The
dice is rolled, and both players write the number in one of their boxes on the
left. After three rolls of the dice, each player has a decimal number. They round
this to the nearest whole number. Score points to match the number of units, e.g.

Materials
A dice

83

| 4 | 6 | · | I | ⟶ | 4 | 6 | (6)

The winner is the one with the highest total score after six rounds

Name _____

Adding decimals

Complete these addition tables.

+	2·7	0·5	1·9	3·8
0·8				
3·6				
2·4				
5·7				

+	1·23	1·86	3·15	2·28
2·45				
3·24				
1·78				
2·09				

84

Name _____

Subtracting decimals

Complete these difference tables.

d	6·7	5·9	2·8	0·7
2·4				
7·9				
1·3				
4·6				

d	6·84	3·04	5·43	1·72
1·91				
2·23				
0·76				
3·95				

Name _____  _____

Percentages

Colour each grid to match the percentages.

I.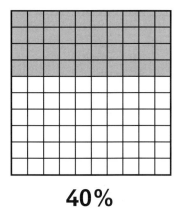

40%

2.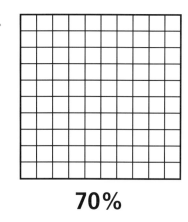

70%

3.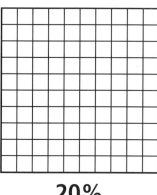

20%

4.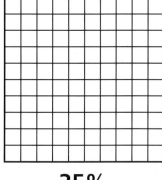

35%

5.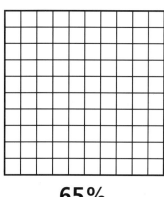

65%

6.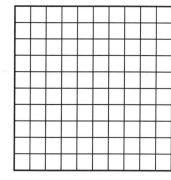

72%

7.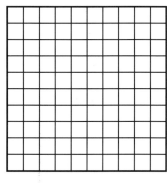

18%

8.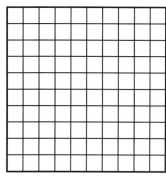

94%

q.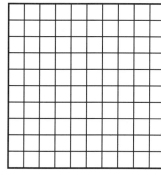

51%

Name _____

Percentages

50%	$\dfrac{9}{10}$	**25%**	**20%**
0·75	$\dfrac{2}{10}$	**0·4**	**0·3**
$\dfrac{1}{4}$	**40%**	$\dfrac{6}{10}$	**90%**
$\dfrac{3}{6}$	**10%**	$\dfrac{3}{4}$	**0·50**
0·6	**0·20**	**0·25**	$\dfrac{4}{10}$
60%	$\dfrac{1}{5}$	**0·9**	**75%**

Teacher's instructions
Cut out the cards and sort them into equal sets.
A game for two players. Shuffle the cards and deal one each.
The player with the card of highest value collects both cards. If the cards are
equal, collect one each.
Continue until all the cards have been collected. Who collected the most?

87

Problem page

1. The garden centre has 139 tulips for sale. They are planted in tubs of 6. How many are left over? How many tubs are for sale?

2. The Reader family saves newspapers for recycling. They save one newspaper every day. How many weeks will it take them to collect 130 papers?

3. There is a sale at the bookshop. All books are sold at 50% of the normal price. What does it cost to buy three books whose original prices were £2·10, £1·85 and £1·25?

4. 50% of a mystery number is 2 less than 10. What is the number?

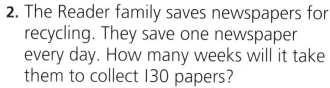

5. What is the difference between 50% of 42p and $\frac{2}{3}$ of 60p?

6. It is 3·7 km from Jody's house to the post-office if he walks along the pavement. It is 2·9 km if he takes a short cut through the park. How many metres less is it to walk through the park? How far is it to go along the pavement, and come back through the park?

7. Kim's meal costs £3·68, Jake's £5·32 and Mai-lin's £4·75. How much more does Jake's meal cost than each of the others? How much change will there be from £20 for the total bill?

8. Two numbers have a total of 10 and a difference of 1·4. What are the numbers?

Name _____

The next whole number

Write each pointed number, then add
to it to make the next whole number.

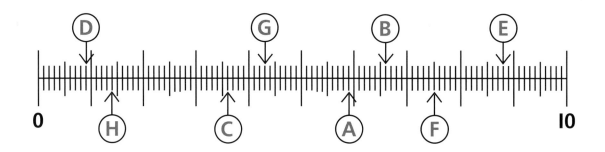

A   _5·9_ + _0·1_ = _6_   B   _____ + _____ = _____

C   _____ + _____ = _____   D   _____ + _____ = _____

E   _____ + _____ = _____   F   _____ + _____ = _____

G   _____ + _____ = _____   H   _____ + _____ = _____

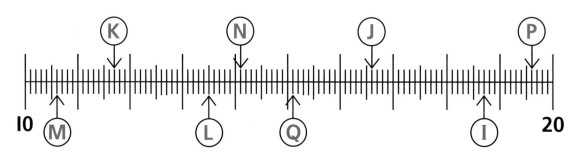

I   _____ + _____ = _____   J   _____ + _____ = _____

K   _____ + _____ = _____   L   _____ + _____ = _____

M   _____ + _____ = _____   N   _____ + _____ = _____

P   _____ + _____ = _____   Q   _____ + _____ = _____

The next whole number

Write the missing number.

1. ( ) $+ 0.6 = 2.0$

2. ( ) $+ 0.1 = 4.0$

3. ( ) $+ 0.8 = 7.0$

4. ( ) $+ 0.5 = 3.0$

5. ( ) $+ 0.2 = 5.0$

6. ( ) $+ 0.9 = 8.0$

7. ( ) $+ 0.7 = 3.0$

8. ( ) $+ 0.4 = 1.0$

9. ( ) $+ 0.1 = 9.0$

10. ( ) $+ 0.3 = 4.0$

11. ( ) $+ 0.5 = 5.0$

12. ( ) $+ 0.7 = 6.0$

13. ( ) $+ 0.8 = 1.0$

14. ( ) $+ 0.2 = 2.0$

15. ( ) $+ 0.3 = 6$

16. ( ) $+ 0.4 = 7$

17. ( ) $+ 0.6 = 4$

18. ( ) $+ 0.4 = 3$

19. ( ) $+ 0.5 = 2$

20. ( ) $+ 0.9 = 8$

Name _____

Adding

Estimate the total, then add.

1. ⬭
```
  1 · 5  2
+ 2 · 3  6
_____
```

2. ⬭
```
  1 · 7  8
+ 2 · 4  5
_____
```

3. ⬭
```
  7 · 5  2
+ 8 · 3  6
_____
```

4. ⬭
```
  3 · 2  8
+ 1 · 9  5
_____
```

5. ⬭
```
  2 · 7  6
+ 3 · 4  1
_____
```

6. ⬭
```
  5 · 8  6
+ 2 · 3  5
_____
```

7. ⬭
```
  6 · 4  2
  5 · 3  1
+ 2 · 4  7
_____
```

8. ⬭
```
  5 · 1  8
  2 · 9  7
+ 1 · 0  8
_____
```

9. ⬭
```
  4 · 5  6
  3 · 8  7
+ 6 · 9  2
_____
```

10. ⬭
```
  3 · 1  7
  4 · 8  6
+ 1 · 0  9
_____
```

11. ⬭
```
  2 · 0  8
  3 · 9  5
+ 0 · 7  2
_____
```

12. ⬭
```
  1 1 · 4  6
    9 · 7  4
+   5 · 4  8
_____
```

91

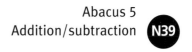

Adding

round 1

☐ . ☐☐
+ ☐ . ☐☐
_____

_____

score ☐

round 2

☐ . ☐☐
+ ☐ . ☐☐
_____

_____

score ☐

round 3

☐ . ☐☐
+ ☐ . ☐☐
_____

_____

score ☐

round 4

☐ . ☐☐
+ ☐ . ☐☐
_____

_____

score ☐

round 5

☐ . ☐☐
+ ☐ . ☐☐
_____

_____

score ☐

round 6

☐ . ☐☐
+ ☐ . ☐☐
_____

_____

score ☐

Teacher's instructions
A game for two or more players, each with a copy of this scoresheet. Throw the
dice 6 times in each round. After each throw, all the players write the number in
one of their boxes. After the third throw the players add the two numbers
together. The player with the largest total scores 4 points, the next largest 3
points, and so on. The winner is the one with the most points after 6 rounds.

Materials
A dice

92

Name _____

Using known facts

325   +   148   =   473

753   –   148   =   605

148   +   148   =   296

Use the above facts to complete these.

1. Double 148 is _____ .

2. 325 more than 148 is _____ .

3. The difference between 148 and 473 is _____ .

4. Half of 296 is _____.

5. The total of 148 and 605 is _____ .

6. 148 subtracted from 753 is _____ .

7. 473 is 148 more than _____ .

8. 753 take away 605 is _____ .

9. 148 and 605 have a total of _____ .

10. 325 differs from 473 by _____ .

11. 148 is _____ less than 753.

Name _____

Subtracting decimals

For each subtraction, throw a dice three times.
The first throw gives the number of units.
The second throw gives the number of tenths.
The third throw gives the number of hundredths.

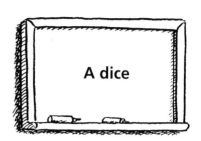

A dice

1. 8 · 6 7

− ☐ · ☐ ☐

_____

2. 9 · 8 7

− ☐ · ☐ ☐

_____

3. 7 · 8 6

− ☐ · ☐ ☐

_____

4. 6 · 7 8

− ☐ · ☐ ☐

_____

5. 8 · 8 9

− ☐ · ☐ ☐

_____

6. 9 · 9 7

− ☐ · ☐ ☐

_____

7. 7 · 9 8

− ☐ · ☐ ☐

_____

8. 8 · 7 6

− ☐ · ☐ ☐

_____

9. 7 · 6 7

− ☐ · ☐ ☐

_____

10. 6 · 9 8

− ☐ · ☐ ☐

_____

11. 6 · 8 9

− ☐ · ☐ ☐

_____

12. 9 · 7 8

− ☐ · ☐ ☐

_____

Name _____

Subtracting decimals

Complete these.

1.
```
  4 5 · 6
- 2 1 · 2
```

2.
```
  3 8 · 9
- 1 4 · 3
```

3.
```
  2 3 · 8
- 1 2 · 6
```

4.
```
  3 6 · 5
- 1 5 · 4
```

5.
```
  2 2 · 1
-   1 · 4
```

6.
```
  1 7 · 5
-   6 · 7
```

7.
```
  5 4 · 2
- 3 3 · 3
```

8.
```
  1 9 · 4
- 1 7 · 6
```

9.
```
  4 4 · 7
- 1 2 · 3
```

10.
```
  3 7 · 3
- 2 3 · 1
```

11.
```
  4 3 · 8
- 3 1 · 7
```

12.
```
  5 6 · 3
- 2 4 · 4
```

13.
```
  3 8 · 5
- 1 3 · 1
```

14.
```
  4 2 · 5
- 2 1 · 9
```

15.
```
  6 5 · 5
- 4 2 · 4
```

16.
```
  7 9 · 2
- 3 8 · 7
```

Subtracting decimals

round 1

```
  ☐ . ☐   ☐
- ☐ . ☐   ☐
─────────────

─────────────
```

score ☐

round 2

```
  ☐ . ☐   ☐
- ☐ . ☐   ☐
─────────────

─────────────
```

score ☐

round 3

```
  ☐ . ☐   ☐
- ☐ . ☐   ☐
─────────────

─────────────
```

score ☐

round 4

```
  ☐ . ☐   ☐
- ☐ . ☐   ☐
─────────────

─────────────
```

score ☐

Total score ☐

Teacher's instructions
A game for two or more players, each with a copy of this scoresheet.
Throw the dice six times in each round. After each throw, all the players write
the number in one of their boxes. After the sixth throw, the players subtract the
bottom number from the top one (checking each other's work). If the top
number is smaller than the bottom number, score 0 points. Otherwise, score the
answer. The winner is the one with most points after four rounds.

Materials
A dice

96

Odds and evens

'O' is odd, 'E' is even.
Write 'O' or 'E' for each.

1. O + O =

2. E + E =

3. E + O =

4. O + E =

5. O – O =

6. E – E =

7. O – E =

8. E – O =

9. E + E + E =

10. E + O + E =

11. O + E + O =

12. O + E – O =

13. E + O – E =

14. E – E + O =

15. O + E + O + E =

16. E + O + O + O =

17. E + E + E + O =

18. O – E + O – E =

19. O + E + O + E + O =

20. E + O + O + E + E =

Square numbers

Complete the number spiral.

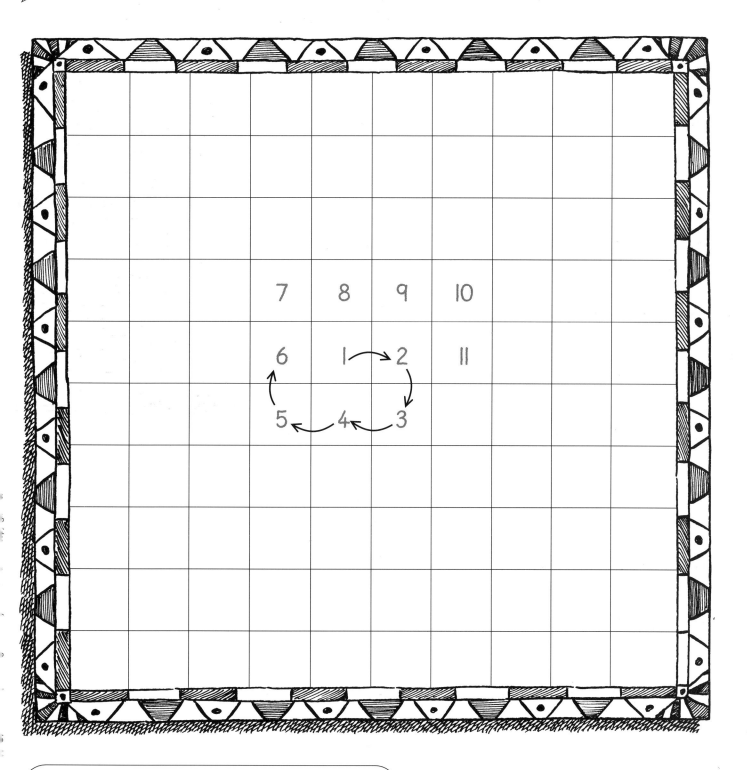

Colour the squares that contain the square numbers. Describe what you notice.

Name _____

Mystery numbers

Use the clues to solve the mystery numbers.
They are all between I and 10.

I.

Square me and my
units digit is 5.

2.

Square me and I am
I less than 10.

3.

Square me and I am
just short of half a
century.

4.

Square me and I
become myself.

5.

Square me and I am
a multiple of 12.

6.

Square me and I am
half of 128.

7.

Square me and my
digit total is 13.

8.

Square me and my
digit difference is 7.

9.

Square me and both
my digits are even.

10.

Square me and I
become a multiple
of 27.

II.

Square me, then
square me again and
I am between 80
and 90.

12.

Square me, then
multiply me by 5,
and I am 20.

Name _____

Length

Write each length in metres, in centimetres and in millimetres.

I. height of road sign ☐ m ☐ cm ☐ mm

2. length of suit ☐ m ☐ cm ☐ mm

3. width of tape player ☐ m ☐ cm ☐ mm

4. length of umbrella ☐ m ☐ cm ☐ mm

5. length of ladder ☐ m ☐ cm ☐ mm

6. height of bus stop sign ☐ m ☐ cm ☐ mm

7. width of bus stop sign ☐ m ☐ cm ☐ mm

Name _____

Length

> Write these in centimetres.

1. $10\,mm =$ [ ] cm

2. $1\frac{1}{2}\,m =$ [ ] cm

3. $1\,m =$ [ ] cm

4. $40\,mm =$ [ ] cm

5. $50\,mm =$ [ ] cm

6. $1{\cdot}4\,m =$ [ ] cm

7. $120\,mm =$ [ ] cm

8. $15\,mm =$ [ ] cm

> Write these in millimetres.

9. $1\,cm =$ [ ] mm

10. $1\,m =$ [ ] mm

11. $\frac{1}{2}\,m =$ [ ] mm

12. $\frac{1}{2}\,cm =$ [ ] mm

13. $3\,cm =$ [ ] mm

14. $2\,cm\ 3\,mm =$ [ ] mm

15. $3{\cdot}4\,cm =$ [ ] mm

16. $2{\cdot}3\,cm =$ [ ] mm

> Write these in metres.

17. $100\,cm =$ [ ] m

18. $150\,cm =$ [ ] m

19. $1000\,mm =$ [ ] m

20. $270\,cm =$ [ ] m

21. $300\,cm =$ [ ] m

22. $50\,cm =$ [ ] m

23. $2000\,mm =$ [ ] m

24. $137\,cm =$ [ ] m

101

Name _____

Miles and kilometres

Write < or > between each pair.

3 miles is
about 5 kilometres.

1. 5 miles  10 km

2. 10 km  10 miles

3. 12 miles  25 km

4. 4 miles  5 km

5. 50 km  20 miles

6. 1 mile  2 km

7. $\frac{1}{2}$ km  1 mile

8. 4 km  3 miles

9. 20 km  15 miles

10. 15 km  20 miles

11. 30 km 25 miles

12. 50 km 40 miles

13. 60 miles 80 km

14. 100 km 50 miles

15. 12 miles 30 km

16. 6 miles 9 km

Name _____

Grams and kilograms

Write each weight in grams.

1.
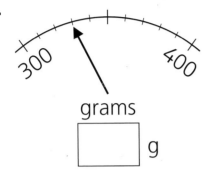

grams

☐ g

2.
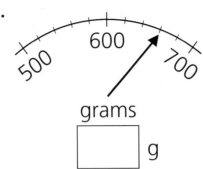

grams

☐ g

3.
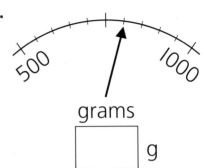

grams

☐ g

4.
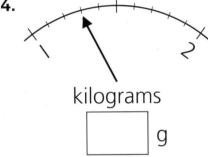

kilograms

☐ g

5.
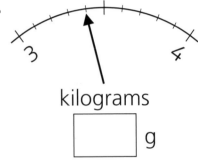

kilograms

☐ g

6.
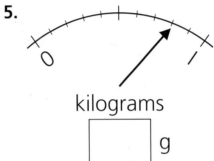

kilograms

☐ g

7.
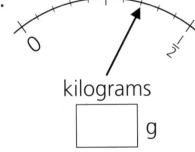

kilograms

☐ g

8.
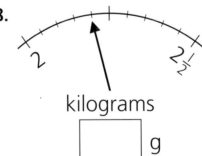

kilograms

☐ g

9.
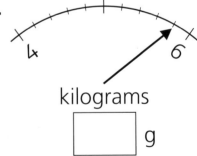

kilograms

☐ g

10.
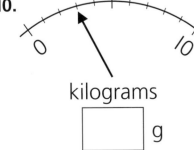

kilograms

☐ g

11.
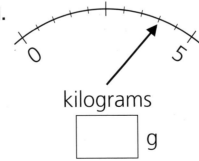

kilograms

☐ g

12.
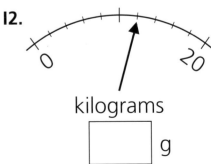

kilograms

☐ g

Name _____

Area of a rectangle

Draw rectangles with these areas.

1.

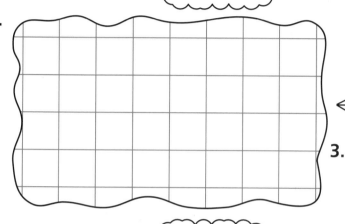

A = 15 cm²

2.

A = 8 cm²

3.

A = 20 cm²

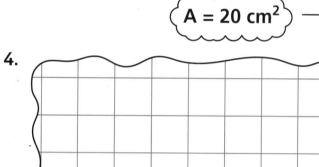

4.

A = 12 cm²

5.

A = 18 cm²

6.

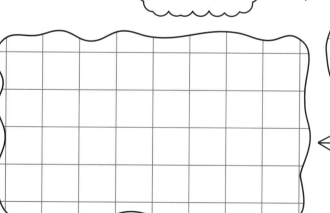

A = 16 cm²

Name _____

Holes

Each card has a hole.   Write the area of each card.   All measurements are in centimetres.

1.

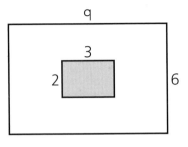

A = ☐ cm²

2.

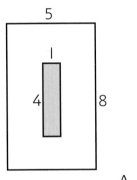

A = ☐ cm²

3.

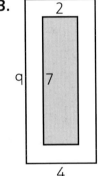

A = ☐ cm²

4.

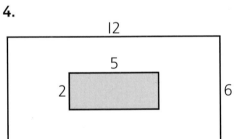

A = ☐ cm²

5.

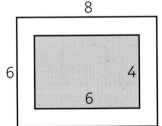

A = ☐ cm²

6.

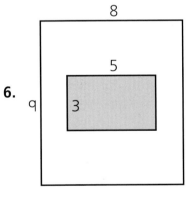

A = ☐ cm²

Name _____

Perimeter

> Write the perimeter of each rectangle.
> All measurements are in centimetres.

3·4

A | 1·5

3

B | 4·6

1·6

C | 1·7

3·5

D | 2·1

5·2

0·9 | **E**

4·3

F | 4·3

1·3

G | 7·4

0·8

5·5 **H**

7·9

1·7 | **I**

11·6

0·6 | **J**

Rectangle	A	B	C	D	E	F	G	H	I	J
Perimeter (cm)										

Name _____

Perimeter

> Estimate the order of the shapes, from the largest perimeter to the smallest perimeter.

	largest					smallest
Estimate						
Measurement						

> Measure, then write the perimeter of each shape. Was your estimated order correct?

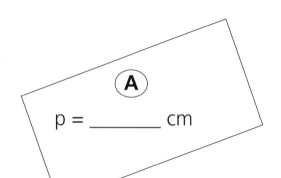

Ⓐ p = _____ cm

Ⓑ p = _____ cm

Ⓒ p = _____ cm

Ⓓ p = _____ cm

Ⓔ p = _____ cm

Ⓕ p = _____ cm

Name _____

Litres, pints and gallons

Write < or > between each pair.

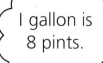 I gallon is 8 pints.

  I litre is a bit less than 2 pints.

1. I litre I pint

2. 2 litres  6 pints

3. 5 pints 2 litres

4. 10 pints  4 litres

5. 10 litres 15 pints

6. 14 pints 5 litres

7. 3 pints  2 litres

8. 9 pints 3 litres

9. 20 litres 30 pints

10. 15 litres 50 pints

11. 10 pints I gallon

12. 30 pints 4 gallons

13. 50 litres 80 pints

14. 150 pints 100 litres

15. $\frac{1}{2}$ gallon 4 litres

16. 5 gallons 15 litres

Name _____

Seconds, minutes, hours, days, weeks, months, years

Write how many minutes.

1. $1\frac{1}{2}$ hours = ☐ minutes

2. 10 hours = ☐ minutes

3. 300 seconds = ☐ minutes

4. $\frac{1}{2}$ day = ☐ minutes

Write how many seconds.

5. 2 minutes = ☐ seconds

6. $3\frac{1}{2}$ minutes = ☐ seconds

7. 10 minutes = ☐ seconds

8. 1 min 35 seconds = ☐ seconds

Write how many hours.

9. 150 minutes = ☐ hours

10. 2 days = ☐ hours

11. 1 week = ☐ hours

12. 3600 seconds = ☐ hours

Write how many days.

13. 2 weeks = ☐ days

14. 60 hours = ☐ days

15. January = ☐ days

16. $\frac{1}{2}$ year = ☐ days

Name _____

24-hour clock

Write these afternoon and
evening times as 24-hour times.

1.

```
1 3 : 1 5
```

2.

⬚ : ⬚

3.

⬚ : ⬚

4.

⬚ : ⬚

5.

⬚ : ⬚

6.

⬚ : ⬚

7.

⬚ : ⬚

8.

⬚ : ⬚

9.

⬚ : ⬚

10.

⬚ : ⬚

11.

⬚ : ⬚

12.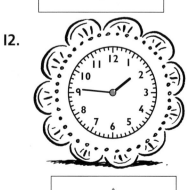

⬚ : ⬚

Name _____

a.m. and p.m.

Write these times as a.m. or p.m.

I.

`19:30`

7 : 30 pm

2.

`03:20`

3.

`17:40`

4.

`10:50`

5.

`08:10`

6.

`20:15`

7.

`11:45`

8.

`16:25`

`15:35`

I0.

`05:55`

II.

`06:15`

I2.

`13:25`

III

Name _____

Parallel

Make these shapes with parallel sides.

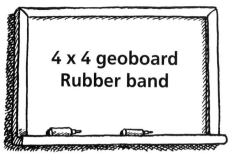

**4 x 4 geoboard
Rubber band**

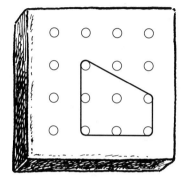
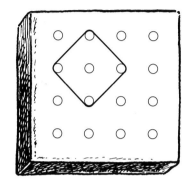
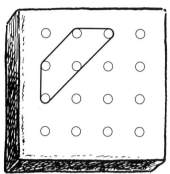

Make some more shapes with parallel sides.

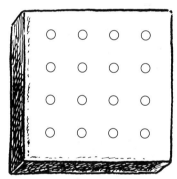

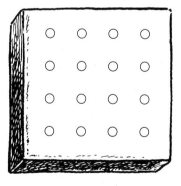

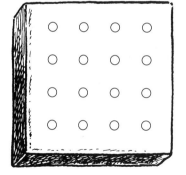

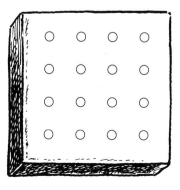

Name _____

Mystic rose

Draw all the diagonals of this regular 12-sided polygon (dodecagon).
The pattern you create is called a mystic rose.

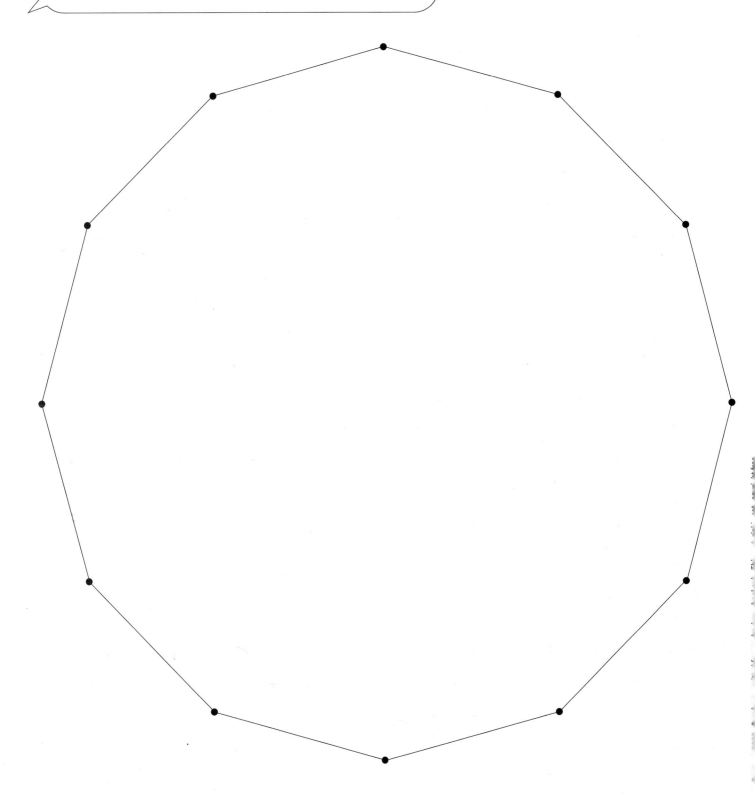

Name _____

Types of triangle

Colour:
the **right-angled** triangles orange,
the **isosceles** triangles red,
the **equilateral** triangles blue,
the **scalene** triangles yellow.

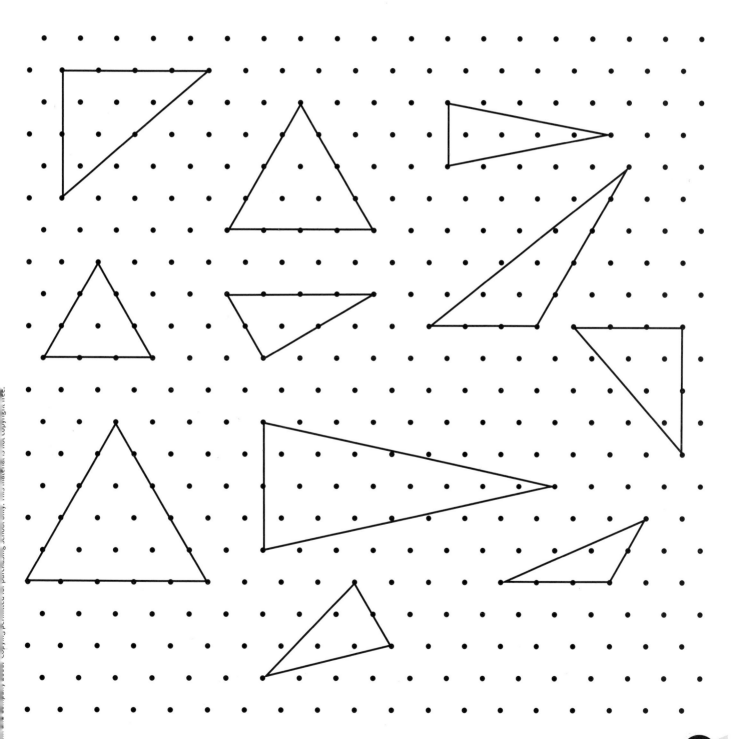

Name _____

Symmetry

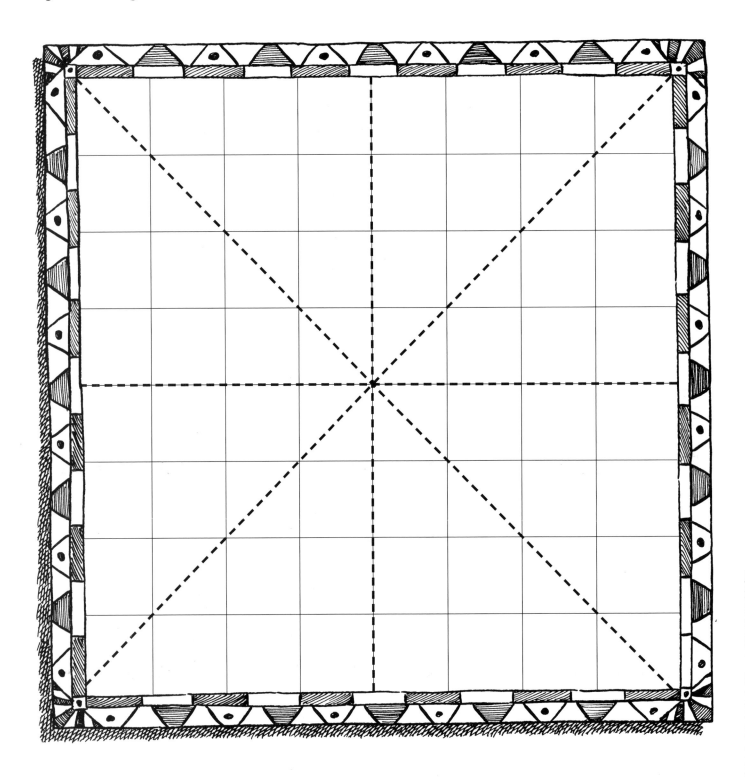

Teacher's instructions

A game for three players.

The first person places a counter on any square. The second person places another counter on a position that is symmetrical to the first about one of the lines. The third person has to say which is the line of symmetry. Swap roles.

Materials
Set of counters of the same colour

e The first person places two or three counters.

Name _____

Symmetry

Complete each shape by drawing its reflection in the line of symmetry.

I.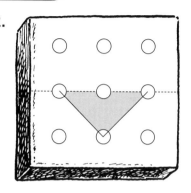

2.

3.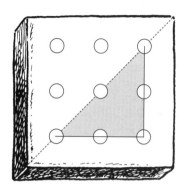

4.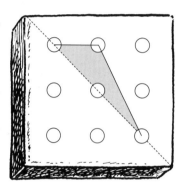

5.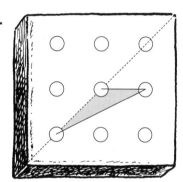

6.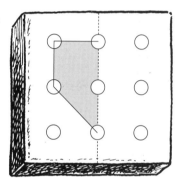

7.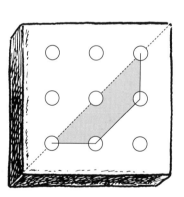

8.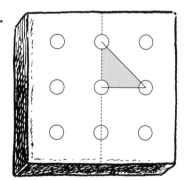

q.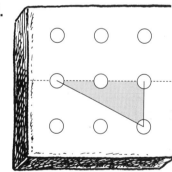

10.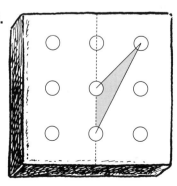

II.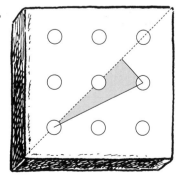

12.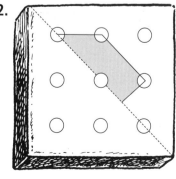

Naming shapes

Write the name of each shape.

I.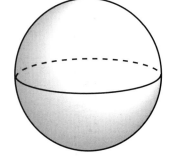

2.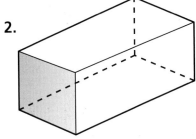

3.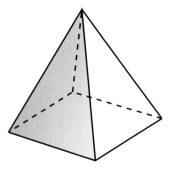

_____

4.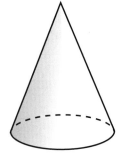

5.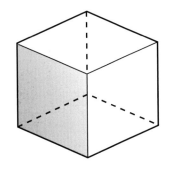

6.

_____

7.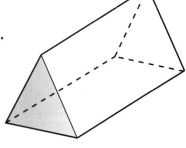

8.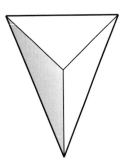

q.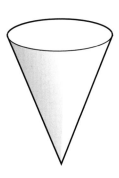

_____

10.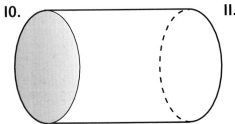

II.

12.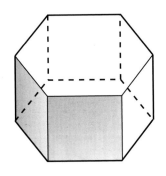

_____

Name _____

Net of a prism

Cut, fold and glue this
net to make a prism.

**Scissors
Glue**

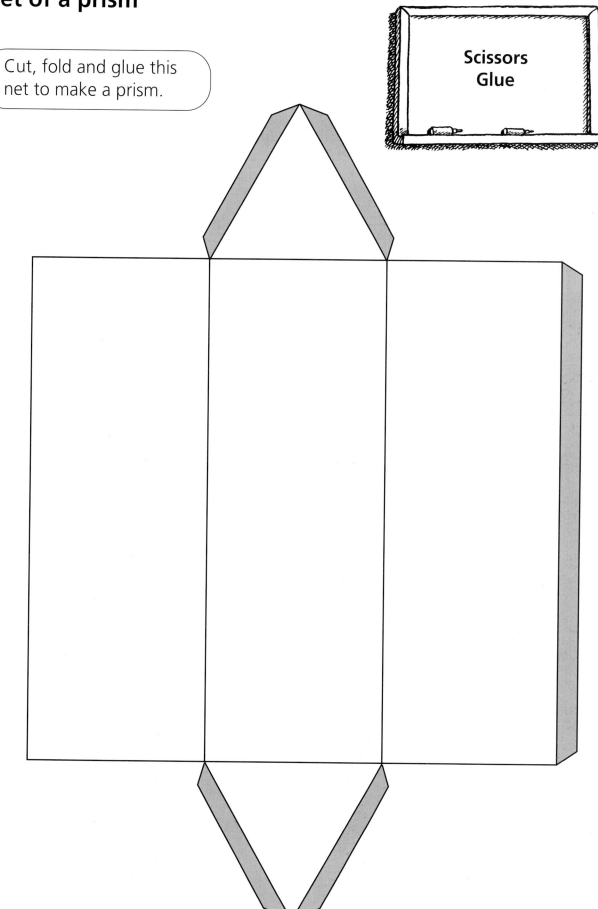

Name _____

Rotations

Draw each pattern after each of four quarter turns.

1.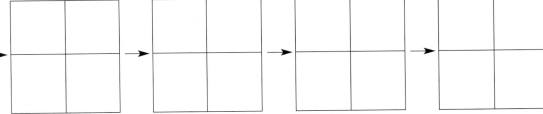

2.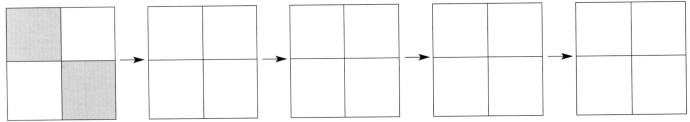

3.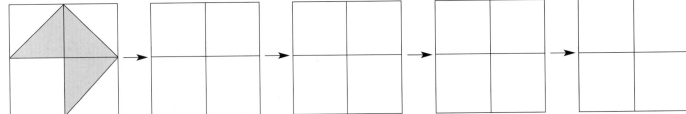

4.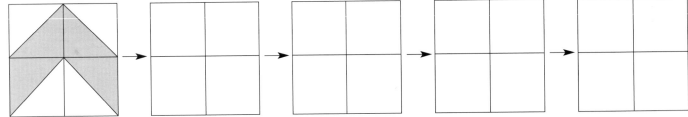

5.

6.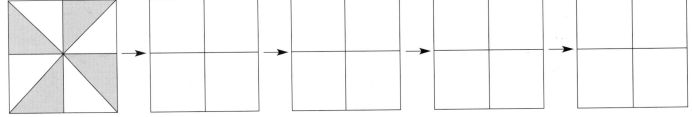

Coordinates

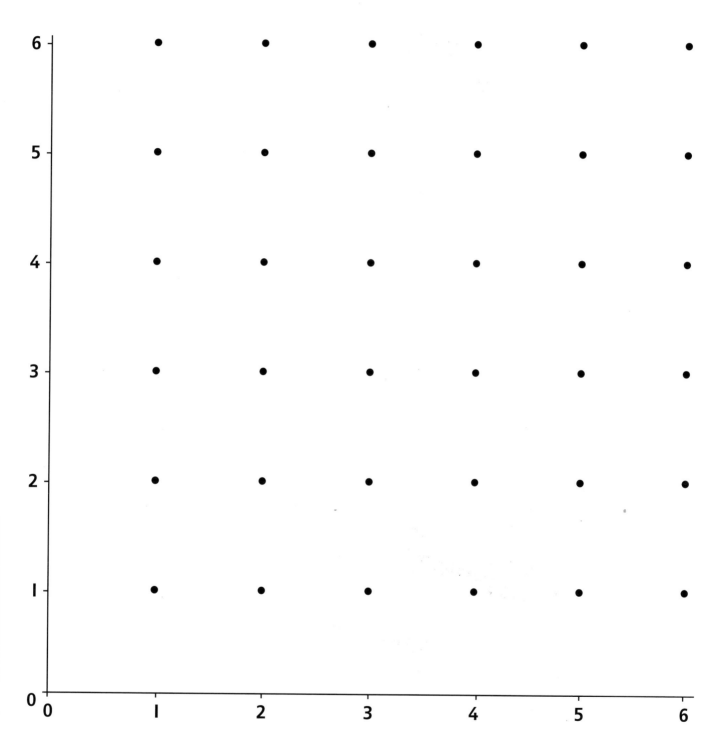

Teacher's instructions
A game for two players.
One dice represents the 'along' coordinate, and the other represents the 'up' coordinate.
Take turns to throw the dice, and place one of your counters on the matching point on the grid. The winner is the first to place three counters in a straight line.

Materials
2 dice of different colours
Set of counters each

120

Name _____

Angles

> Write the missing angles.

I.

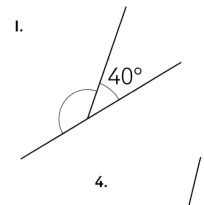
40°

2.

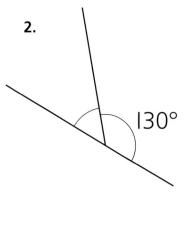
130°

3.

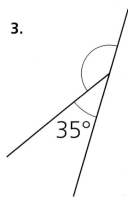
35°

4.

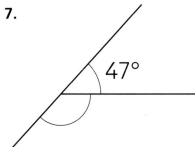
76°

5.

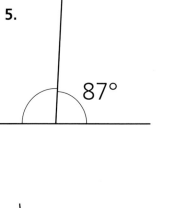
87°

6.

32°

7.

47°

8.

119°

q.

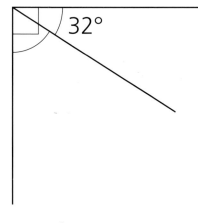
131°

10.

67°

II.

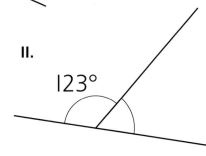
123°

Name _____

Measuring angles

Estimate the order of these angles, smallest to largest.

Write the letter.

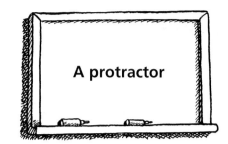

A protractor

	smallest							largest
Estimate								
Measure								

Then measure and write the size of each.

Was your order correct?

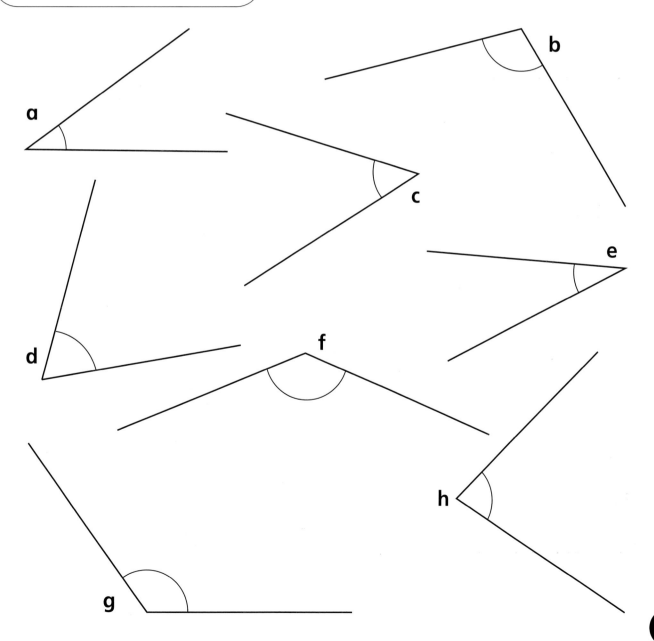

Name _____

Types of angle

Colour:
the **acute** angles red,
the **obtuse** angles blue,
the **reflex** angles yellow.

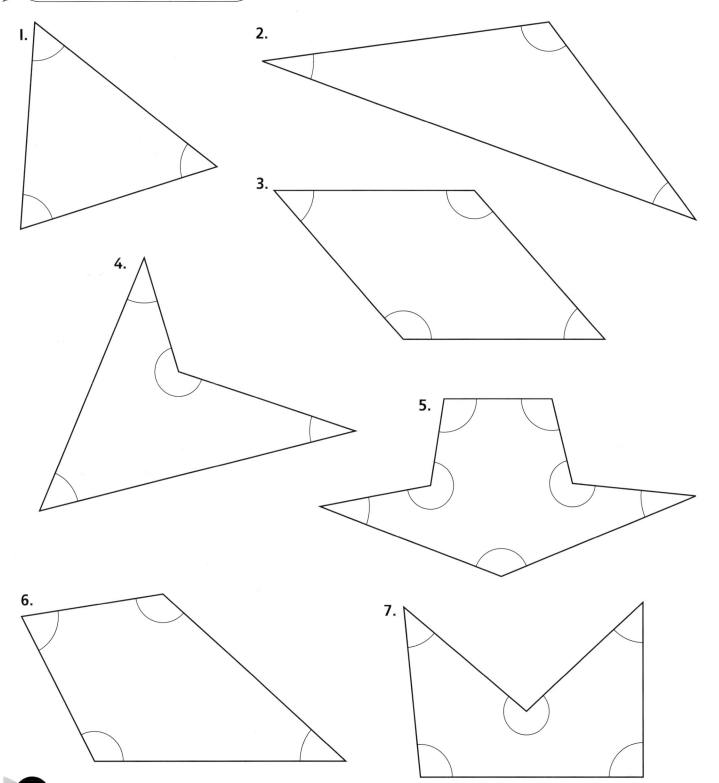

1.

2.

3.

4.

5.

6.

7.

Types of angle

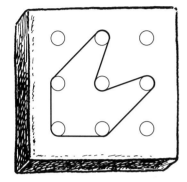
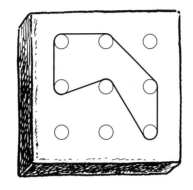
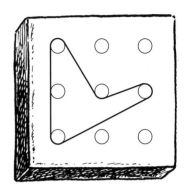

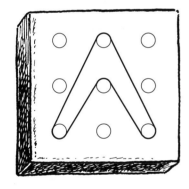
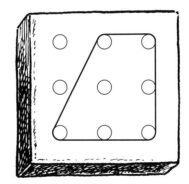
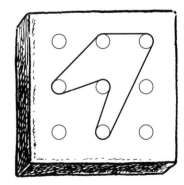

Teacher's instructions
A game for two players. Take turns to throw the dice, and colour one of the angles in the shape for that dice number. If the angle is:
acute, colour it red and score 1 point
obtuse, colour it blue and score 12 points
right-angled, colour it orange and score 3 points
reflex, colour it yellow and score 4 points.

Materials
A dice
4 coloured pens: red, blue, orange, yellow

Name _____

Bar-line graphs

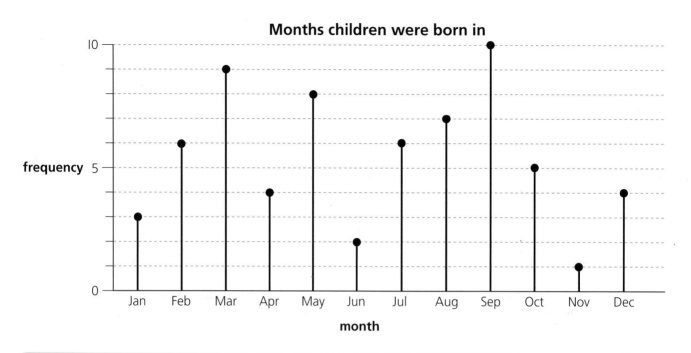

The graph shows the months in which some children were born.
How many were born in:

1. May? ☐   **2.** June? ☐   **3.** December? ☐

In which month were these numbers of children born:

4. 5? ☐   **5.** 3? ☐   **6.** 9? ☐

How many more children were born in:

7. February than April? ☐   **8.** August than November? ☐

In which month were:

9. most born? ☐   **10.** fewest born? ☐

How many children does this graph show altogether? **11.** ☐

How many children were born in:

12. the first 3 months? ☐   **13.** the second 3 months? ☐

14. the next 3 months? ☐   **15.** the last 3 months? ☐

Temperature graph

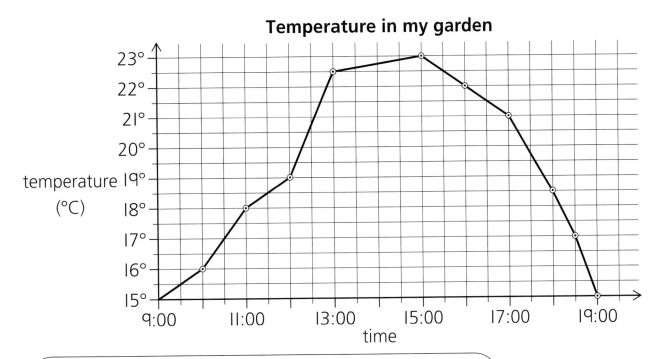

Temperature in my garden

The graph shows the temperature change in a garden.
What is the temperature at:

I. II:00? ☐   **2.** I7:00? ☐   **3.** I2:00? ☐

4. 9:30? ☐   **5.** I5:30? ☐   **6.** I8:00? ☐

At what times is the temperature:

7. $22\frac{1}{2}$ °C? ☐   **8.** I7°C? ☐   **9.** $18\frac{1}{2}$ °C? ☐

How does the temperature change between:

I0. II o'clock and 3 o'clock? ☐

II. 3 o'clock and 7 o'clock? ☐

I2. half-past 9 and noon? ☐

Name _____

Ticks

Tick the box to describe the chances of these happening.

	impossible	unlikely	likely	certain
1. Christmas Day will be in January.				
2. Tonight there will be a storm.				
3. The next person who comes into the room will be a girl.				
4. Tomorrow it will rain.				
5. One day, I will fly a plane.				
6. The next car I see will be red.				
7. I will sneeze today.				
8. The Sun will move around the Earth.				
9. Next year I will be one day older.				
10. Next week will have seven days.				

Invent 10 of your own statements and tick a box for each.

Abacus Ginn and Company 2000. Copying permitted for purchasing school only. This material is not copyright free.